DATE			

Francis Bacon's
Philosophy of Science

Francis Bacon's Philosophy of Science:
An Account and a Reappraisal

Peter Urbach

Open ❄ Court
La Salle, Illinois

OPEN COURT and the above logo are registered in the
U.S. Patent & Trademark Office.

© 1987 by Open Court Publishing Company.

First printing 1987.

Printed and bound in the United States of America.

Library of Congress Cataloging-in-Publication Data

Urbach, Peter.
  Francis Bacon's philosophy of science.

  Bibliography: p.
  1. Bacon, Francis, 1561-1626—Knowledge—Science.
2. Science—Philosophy. 3. Scientists—Great Britain—
Biography. I. Title.
Q143.B223U73 1986   509'.2'4   85-25947
ISBN 0-912050-44-6
ISBN 0-8216-9015-X (pbk.)

Contents

Acknowledgements   viii

Introduction: Bacon's Life and Writings   1
   A Brief Survey of Bacon's Life   1
   Sources for Bacon's Life   6
   Bacon's Writings   7
   References in this Book to Bacon's Writings   11
   The General Character of Bacon's Philosophy   13

Chapter One: The Standard Interpretation   17
   1(i)   The Infallible-Mechanical Thesis   17
   1(ii)   How Good is Bacon's Method, According to its
        Standard Interpretation?   20

Chapter Two: Bacon's Principles of Induction   25
   2(i)   Introduction   25
   2(ii)   The Anticipation and Interpretation of Nature   26
   2(iii)   The Anticipation of Nature and Conventionalism   30
   2(iv)   The Role of Hypotheses   33
   2(v)   Epicurus on Anticipation   37
   2(vi)   Certainty and Bacon's Method   38
       (a)   The Infallibility Thesis   38
       (b)   On the Prospect of Proving the Principles of
           Induction   39
       (c)   A Game-Theoretic Argument   42
       (d)   Certainty as an Extreme Degree of
           Confidence   43
       (e)   Ideas of Inductive Proof in Bacon's Time   44
       (f)   Bacon's Opposition to Conjectures   46
       (g)   Summary   49
   2(vii)   Appraising Bacon's Method   49
       (a)   The Interpretation of Nature and
           Falsificationism   49
       (b)   The Plausibility of Bacon's Theory   51
       (c)   Some Difficulties in Bacon's Theory   52
   2(viii)   Summary   56

Chapter Three: The Aims of Baconian Science   59
   3(i)   Speculative and Operative Science   59
   3(ii)   Physics   60
           (a) Efficient and Material Causes   60
           (b) Latent Configurations and Processes   60
   3(iii)   Metaphysics and the Nature of Forms   61
           (a) Forms   61
           (b) Examples of Forms: Colour and Heat   63
   3(iv)   Forms as Ideals   66
   3(v)   Forms of the First and Second Class   69
   3(vi)   Atomism   72
           (a) Introduction   72
           (b) Two Kinds of Atomism   72
           (c) Did Bacon Change his Mind on Atomism?   76
   3(vii) Bacon's Views on the Vacuum   79
   3(viii) Conclusion   81

Chapter Four: The Idols   83
   4(i)   Introduction   83
   4(ii)   The Idols of the Tribe and of the Cave   85
   4(iii)   The Idols of the Market-place   92
   4(iv)   The Idols of the Theatre   95
   4(v)   The Idols of Superstition   98
           (a) Science and Superstition   98
           (b) Final Causes   100
           (c) Science and Religion   102
   4(vi)   Summary   105

Chapter Five: Bacon's Assessment of the Science of His Day   107
   5(i)   Introduction   107
   5(ii)   William Gilbert and Magnetism   109
   5(iii)   Astrology   121
   5(iv)   Alchemy   125
   5(v)   Astronomy   125
   5(vi)   Mathematics   134
   5(vii) Biology   143
   5(viii) Summary   148

Chapter Six: The Role of Experiment   149
  6(i)   Introduction   149
  6(ii)   Four Common Criticisms of Bacon's
          Experimental Philosophy   150
          (a) On the Importance of Histories   151
          (b) Should All the Facts be Collected?   153
          (c) The Relation of Theory to Fact   154
          (d) On the Corrigibility of Histories   156
  6(iii) Constructing the Histories   160
  6(iv) Prerogative Instances   164
          (a) Prerogative Instances Useful for the Initial
              Survey of Phenomena   164
          (b) Prerogative Instances Useful for the
              Induction of Axioms   166
          (c) Summary   171
  6(v)   The Tables of Instances and the Example
          of Heat   172
  6(vi)   Tables of Degrees   176
  6(vii) The Commencement of Interpretation, or the
          First Vintage   178
  6(viii) The Role and Purpose of the First Vintage   181
  6(ix)   Summary   183

Chapter Seven: Conclusion   187

Bibliography   193

Index   199

Acknowledgements

I have pleasure in thanking a number of my friends and colleagues, who were kind enough to read this book in draft, and who made many valuable suggestions for improvement. They are Ian Box, Jon Dorling, Mary Hesse, Colin Howson, Peter Milne, and, especially, Kurt Klappholz. I also gained from discussions with Richard McKirahan. However, I alone am responsible for the views expressed herein.

I also wish to thank Sue Burrett and Gay Woolven for their friendly and expert assistance in preparing the various drafts and final typescript of this book, and to acknowledge the painstaking work of editing by the staff of the Open Court Publishing Company. I am grateful for the help which I received from Elizabeth Wrigley and Jacqueline Bellows of the Francis Bacon Library, Claremont, California, and from Youssef Aliabadi.

I gratefully acknowledge support from the Suntory-Toyota International Centre for Economics and Related Disciplines, which enabled me to take leave of absence from teaching, while writing this book; from The British Academy; and from the Central Research Fund of London University.

Finally, I wish to thank David Urbach. And I especially want to express my gratitude to Alasdair Cameron for research assistance and friendship.

Peter Urbach, 1986

Francis Bacon's
Philosophy of Science

Introduction
Bacon's Life and Writings

*Si tabula daretur digna,
animum (If one could but paint
his mind!)* (Nicholas Hilliard)

A Brief Survey of Bacon's Life

Francis Bacon was born on 22 January 1561, or 1560 by a convention of the time which reckoned 25 March as the start of the civil year. He died on Easter morning, 1626, having achieved fame and distinction in politics, the law, letters, and philosophy.

Bacon was descended from a very distinguished family. His father, Sir Nicholas Bacon, was one of Queen Elizabeth's most eminent councillors, occupying the office of Lord Keeper of the Great Seal, while his mother was an accomplished scholar, related, by the marriage of her sister, to Sir William Cecil (later Lord Burleigh), the Queen's Secretary of State.

Bacon attended Trinity College, Cambridge, from the age of twelve, a little earlier than was normal, and he studied there for nearly three years, under the tutelage of John Whitgift, who later rose to be Archbishop of Canterbury. At the age of fifteen, Bacon commenced law studies at Gray's Inn, in London, a course which was apparently envisaged as the springboard for the career of a statesman. There was, however, another strand to his ambition, namely, to be a philosopher and reformer of natural philosophy. The idea that he could make a mark in philosophy and that urgent reform was required in that area occurred to him while he was still at Cambridge, where "he first fell into the dislike of the philosophy of Aristotle". As he related to his chaplain, Dr William Rawley (1657, 4), this dislike was "not for the worthlessness of the author, to whom he would ever ascribe all high attributes, but for the unfruitfulness of the way; being a philosophy (as his Lordship used to say) only strong for disputations and contentions, but barren of the production of works for the benefit of the life of man; in which mind he continued to his dying day."

Bacon took the first steps in his professional career in 1576 when, interrupting his studies at Gray's Inn, he accompanied Sir Amias Paulet to France, where that gentleman had been newly appointed resident ambassador. We cannot be certain exactly how Bacon was occupied during this time, but he evidently acquitted himself "with great approbation" (Rawley, 1657, 4). Unhappily for him, though, his father died, suddenly, in 1579, leaving him ill provided for, and he was obliged to return to England. He now took up his legal training in earnest and, after three years, became 'utter barrister', or junior counsel, and, after seven years, bencher, which entitled him to plead in the courts of Westminster.

Bacon began his public life in 1584 by entering Parliament, evidently gaining a seat through the influence of his uncle, Lord Burleigh. He seems to have played an active part in parliamentary debates and to have made a considerable impression by the power of his oratory. Indeed, he always took great pains over speeches and wrote brief, and still useful, notes on the art of public speaking (*Works* VII, 109-10), as well as an essay on the subject

(*Of Discourse*).* Ben Jonson (1641, 590–1) judged him to be one of the most accomplished orators of the day:

> there hapn'd, in my time, one noble *Speaker,* who was full of gravity in his speaking. His language, (where hee could spare, or passe by a jest) was nobly *censorious.* No man ever spake more neatly, more presly, more weightily, or suffer'd lesse emptinesse, less idlenesse, in what hee utter'd. No member of his speech, but consisted of his own graces: His hearers could not cough, or looke aside from him, without losse. Hee commanded where hee spoke; and had his Judges angry, and pleased at his devotion. No man had their affections more in his power. The feare of every man that heard him, was, lest hee should make an end.

However, one notable intervention, in the parliament of 1593, when Bacon set himself against the Queen's express wishes, suddenly blighted his prospects for promotion. The Queen required extra funds in order to meet a renewed threat from Spain, this time even more alarming than that from the Armada of 1588, in view of the rumoured collusion of the enemy with certain forces in Scotland. The members of Parliament were asked to approve a triple subsidy, payable in three years, a measure doubly unprecedented in that hitherto each parliament had raised a single subsidy, with two years allowed for payment.

Bacon was prominent in opposition to some details of the proposal, arguing that the country could not afford so steep a rise in taxation and, hence, that attempts to collect it would breed discontent and thereby threaten the Queen's safety. Bacon was outvoted, however, and in the event his fears proved unfounded. But the Queen was greatly displeased by the stand he had taken and, despite urgent entreaties on his behalf by the Earl of Essex, Elizabeth thereafter refused advancement to Bacon, though she never quite quenched his expectations; a useful trick, which she often employed to great advantage. Even though an abject

---

*My method of referring to Bacon's writings is explained on pages 11–12, below.

apology might have mended his chances, Bacon always
maintained that he had acted rightly in opposing the Queen in
Parliament: "I spake simply and to satisfy my conscience," he said.

One crumb that did drop his way was the reversion of the
Clerkship of the Star Chamber, which, however, did not fall
vacant, and so did not yield him any revenue, for nearly twenty
years. Another was a present of some land from Essex, in
compensation for his failure to secure for Bacon the post of either
Attorney-General or Solicitor-General, and presumably, too, in
order to reward Bacon for his work as a personal advisor, and to
retain him in that capacity.

Bacon had to wait until Elizabeth was succeeded by James for
any substantial preferment and, from 1604, when he was made
one of the King's learned counsel, he steadily rose to Solicitor-
General (1607), Attorney-General (1613), Privy Councillor (1616),
then Lord Keeper of the Great Seal (1617), and finally,
overtopping his father, Lord Chancellor (1618). His dignities
increased at the same time, he being knighted in 1603 (though in
the company of 300 others), then raised to Baron Verulam of
Verulam and finally to Viscount St Alban.

His belated and rapid rise, however, met a sudden and
ignominious end and a precipitate reverse, through a number of
charges of corruption in the performance of his judicial duties,
which were made against him. The first of these surfaced in 1621
and was quickly followed by others, the general burden of the
accusations being that Bacon corruptly accepted bribes, in the
form of money and presents, from some of those who appeared
before him who sought thereby to secure favourable
consideration.

Bacon's health suffered greatly under the strain of these
accusations, but his letters and submissions show that he
nevertheless conducted himself with dignity throughout and,
while he conceded that his practice of accepting gifts from
litigants was wrong, he would not admit that they had corrupted
his judgments. He wrote to the King:

> when the books of hearts shall be opened, I hope I shall not
> be found to have the troubled fountain of a corrupt heart in a
> depraved habit of taking rewards to pervert justice;
> howsoever I may be frail, and partake of the abuse of the
> times. (Spedding, 1878, II, 463)

It is partly because Bacon recognised the essential justice of the complaint against him that he decided to make a full and humble confession and seek for mercy, rather than trying to defend his actions. The consequence was that he was forced out of public life, fined £40,000, and imprisoned in the Tower of London. The fine seems to have been remitted and his incarceration lasted only a few days, but Bacon felt the ignominy of his state bitterly, and petitioned, unsuccessfully, for a royal pardon.

There is some support for Bacon's claim that he was not influenced in his legal judgments by the presents he received, for, as Spedding noted, no record has been discovered of any of his decisions having been reversed. His own reflection on his fate was this:

> I was the justest judge that was in England these fifty years.
> But it was the justest censure in Parliament that was these
> two hundred years. (Spedding, 1878, II, 633)

Thus ended Bacon's professional career. But his life was always, as he said, "divided . . . into the contemplative and active part" (Spedding, 1878, I, 670) and his public disgrace had one consolation, in that he could now devote more time to philosophy. In the five or so years remaining to him, Bacon wrote prolifically and produced some of his most famous works.

Bacon died a famous death. While driving through the snow in the neighbourhood of Highgate, then a small village outside London, Bacon conceived the idea that flesh might be preserved by the cold, just as it is by salt. In order to test that idea, as John Aubrey related, he "alighted out of the Coach and went to a poore woman's house at the bottom of Highgate hill, and bought a Hen, and made the woman exenterate it, and then stuffed the body with Snow, and my Lord [Bacon] did help to doe it himselfe". No doubt the hen was preserved, for Bacon reported that "the experiment itself . . . succeeded excellently well" (Spedding, 1878, II, 620). But the snow had a contrary effect on Bacon, who became extremely ill from the cold. He retired to the Earl of Arundel's house, where he died a few days later, sharing the fate, as he said in the last letter he wrote, of Caius Plinius the elder, who also lost his life by trying an experiment.

It is difficult to believe that the technique of refrigeration was not already well-known. However, it seems not to have been, for Bacon, who had written very extensively on phenomena of preservation and had clearly taken some trouble to inform himself about the subject, had never previously mentioned that refrigeration might prevent the putrefaction of flesh, though he did note that "a flower or an apple [may be preserved] in conservatories of snow; [and] a corpse in balsam" (DA 4ii, 392), and that "salt preserves meat, and that better in winter than summer" (DA 5ii, 417).

Sources for Bacon's Life

The main sources of information on Bacon's life are the short memoir composed by his chaplain, Dr Rawley; Aubrey's *Brief Lives;* and Bacon's own brief autobiographical writings and letters. By far the best life of Bacon is by James Spedding, whose monumental work of editing and biography has not been superseded, and is unlikely to be. Spedding's work is to be found in the following: *The Letters and the Life of Francis Bacon* (seven volumes), 1862–74; *An Account of the Life and Times of Francis Bacon* (two volumes), 1878; and *Evenings with a Reviewer or Macaulay and Bacon* (two volumes), 1881. The first of these contains most of Bacon's surviving letters and speeches and other occasional writings, as well as an exhaustive account of his life. The second is a briefer biography based on the larger work, and the last is a detailed and effective rebuttal of a famous attack made on the moral character of Bacon by Macaulay, in his essay of 1837.

Bacon's Writings

Bacon first established himself as an elegant writer with the publication, in 1597, of a set of essays. These were pithy and beautiful observations with titles such as 'Of Studies', 'Of Followers and Friends', and 'Of Negociating'. The work went through several editions during his life, each enriched with further compositions, until the essays finally numbered fifty-nine. The most authoritative edition is by Michael Kiernan, 1985.

The Great Instauration. Bacon's earliest composition of a more traditionally philosophical character was called *Temporis Partus Maximus* (The Greatest Birth of Time); it was evidently written around 1593, but is now lost. We may guess, however, that it contained his first stab at the project that guided practically all his work in philosophy, namely, a complete reform of the methods by which knowledge was acquired. He referred to this reform as *The Great Instauration* (or 'restoration') and he expected it to be effected by placing a much greater reliance upon observation and experiment than hitherto. *The Great Instauration* was also the title of his magnum opus. This work remained incomplete, but we know its projected shape from the 'Plan of the Great Instauration' which Bacon drew up: this plan is given below, together with a list of those writings which formed a part of it, and the dates on which they were first published.

The Plan of the Great Instauration.
I. *The Divisions of the Sciences.*   This consisted primarily of a review of the contemporary state of knowledge and is represented by the *De Augmentis Scientiarum* (1623), an expanded and revised version, in Latin, of *The Advancement of Learning* (1605).

II. *The New Organon; or Directions concerning the Interpretation of Nature.*   This part, for which the two books of the *Novum Organum* or *New Organon* (1620) were intended, expounds Bacon's new method for the sciences. Although incomplete, this work contains the core of his new philosophy of science.

III. *The Phenomena of the Universe; or a Natural and Experimental History for the Foundation of Philosophy.*   This contains a collection of "experience of every kind, and such a natural history as may serve for a foundation to build philosophy upon." (*Plan*, 28) Bacon composed a number of works intended as contributions to Part III of his great work. They are given below, together with the dates when they were first published:

> *Parasceve ad Historiam et Naturalem* (Preparative towards a
>   Natural and Experimental History) (1620)
> *The History of the Winds* (1622)
> *The History of Life and Death* (1623)
> *The History of Dense and Rare* (1658)
> *Sylva Sylvarum* (usually translated "a collection of
>   collections") (1627)

The first of these works describes the general principles which should guide the selection of a competent collection of observations. The rest were histories of various topics, which Bacon had himself prepared. They comprised observations already known, some original observations from Bacon's own experiments, directions for new experiments, and tentative explanations for some of the phenomena. These works proved enormously popular in the seventeenth century.

IV. *The Ladder of the Intellect.*   This was intended to present examples, from various subjects, of Bacon's method in action, but, like the next two parts of the Plan, it does not seem to have been started by Bacon.

V. *The Forerunners; or Anticipations of the New Philosophy.*   This would have contained investigations carried out, not by the new method, but "by the ordinary use of the understanding" (*Plan*, 31), whose conclusions could therefore be entertained only tentatively.

VI. *The New Philosophy; or Active Science.* This section, whose completion Bacon conceded was "a thing both above my strength and beyond my hopes", "discloses and sets forth that philosophy which by the legitimate, chaste, and severe course of inquiry which I have explained and provided is at length developed and established." (*Plan*, 32)

Early Drafts of The Great Instauration. Bacon worked out his ideas and polished up phrases for *The Great Instauration* over a long period, the *Novum Organum,* for instance, as he told the King, having been nearly thirty years in the writing. We have, indeed, clear evidence of a stage-by-stage development in various pieces composed between 1592 and 1620, but not published in his lifetime. The most important of these are listed below, together with the most probable dates of their composition.

> A *Conference of Pleasure: In Praise of Knowledge* (This was a device in the form of an erudite entertainment presented by the Earl of Essex for the Queen's amusement, but written by Bacon.) (1592)
> *Temporis Partus Masculus* (The Masculine Birth of Time) (1603)
> *Valerius Terminus of the Interpretation of Nature, with Annotations by Hermes Stella* (1603)
> *Cogitationes de Natura Rerum* (Thoughts on the Nature of Things) (1604)
> *Filium Labyrinthi sive Formula Inquisitionis* (This was written in English and is very similar to the next work. Spedding believed that it was composed first. (*Works* III, 495)) (c. 1606)
> *Cogitata et Visa de Interpretatione Naturae* (Thoughts and Conclusions on the Interpretation of Nature) (1607)
> *Redargutio Philosophiarum* (The Refutation of Philosophies) (1608)

Descriptio Globi Intellectualis (A Description of the
   Intellectual Globe) (1612)
Thema Coeli (Theory of the Heaven) (1612)

Additional Writings. Bacon published two other important works
which reflect his philosophical outlook. The first is *De Sapientia
Veterum* (On the Wisdom of the Ancients), in which he
expounded some of the ancient myths concerning Pan,
Prometheus, Cupid, and others. Bacon argued, rather cogently,
that these myths were concealed allegories relating to such
matters as natural philosophy, statecraft, and morals.

> [The fables] must be regarded as neither being the
> inventions nor belonging to the age of the poets themselves,
> but as sacred relics and light airs breathing out of better
> times, that were caught from the traditions of more ancient
> nations and so received into the flutes and trumpets of the
> Greeks. (*Works* VI, 697-8)

Bacon's own versions of the latent meanings of these fables are
often extremely far-fetched, if meant to reflect the original
meanings of their authors. And very often his interpretations
seem simply to be vehicles for expressing his own opinions. The
De Sapientia Veterum was published in 1609; it contains,
incidentally, some of Bacon's finest prose. Bacon considerably
enlarged his explanations of two of the fables, in a work called 'On
Principles and Origins, according to the Fables of Cupid and
Coelum: etc.', which, however, was not printed until after his
death. It seems to have been written some time between 1610 and
1620. (See Rees, 1975, 551, for a discussion of the correct dating of
this work.)

   The New Atlantis is a fable which Bacon himself composed. It
concerns a utopian society that is carefully organised for the
purposes of scientific research and virtuous living. *The New
Atlantis* is often asserted to have provided the inspiration and
model for the Royal Society.

   Bacon was also the author of a notable *History of Henry VII*;
some religious writings, for instance the *Meditationes Sacrae*,

which was published in 1597 in the same volume as his *Essays*;
and a fascinating set of *Apophthegms*, or humorous and pointed
observations and anecdotes, which he dictated from memory
towards the end of his life, and which he had, no doubt, used
throughout his career to ornament his speeches. Many of them
have now lost their witty edge. The following are exceptions,
though, and exemplify the style:

> Queen Elizabeth seeing Sir Edward ———— in her garden,
> looked out at her window, and asked him in Italian, *What
> does a man think of when he thinks of nothing?* Sir Edward
> (who had not had the effect of some of the Queen's grants so
> soon as he had hoped and desired) paused a little, and then
> made answer, *Madam, he thinks of a woman's promise*. The
> Queen shrunk in her head; but was heard to say, *Well, Sir
> Edward, I must not confute you*. Anger makes dull men
> witty, but it keeps them poor. (*Works* VII, 174)

> There was a young man in Rome, that was very like Augustus
> Caesar. Augustus took knowledge of it, and sent for the man,
> and asked him; *Was your mother never at Rome?* He
> answered; *No, sir, but my father was*. (*Works* VII, 138)

Bacon also wrote on questions of state, on legal matters—though
he never achieved his aim of reducing the complexity of English
law to a simple system—and on a variety of other subjects.

References in this Book to Bacon's Writings

The standard edition of Bacon's works is that by James
Spedding, Robert L. Ellis, and Douglas D. Heath, published
between 1857 and 1859 in seven volumes. I shall refer to this
edition as the *Works*. Ellis (1857a) provided it with a useful
preface, in which he gave a general account of Bacon's
philosophical system.

I have, for the most part, relied on the *Works* for translations
from the Latin; on the few occasions where I depart from these, I

indicate as much by placing the original Latin in brackets. Three of Bacon's compositions to which I shall refer were, however, not given in English by Spedding and his colleagues. They are *Thoughts and Conclusions, The Refutation of Philosophies,* and *The Masculine Birth of Time.* Fortunately, this gap has been filled by Benjamin Farrington's excellent work *The Philosophy of Francis Bacon* (1964), to which page-references will be given.

In referring to Bacon's writings, I have adopted the following abbreviations:

DA: *De Augmentis Scientiarum* (*Works* IV, 275–498 and V, 3–119)
NO: *Novum Organum* (*Works* IV, 37–248)
AL: *The Advancement of Learning* (*Works* III, 259–491)
DIG: *A Description of the Intellectual Globe* (*Works* V, 503–44)
TH: *Theory of the Heaven* (*Works* V, 547–59)
Plan: *The Plan of the Great Instauration* (*Works* IV, 22–33)
Sylva: *Sylva Sylvarum* (*Works* II, 333–680)
VT: *Valerius Terminus* (*Works* III, 215–52)
RP: *The Refutation of Philosophies*
TC: *Thoughts and Conclusions*
MBT: *The Masculine Birth of Time*

Apart from the last three items, which are to be found in Farrington (1964), this list also gives the volume (or volumes) in the *Works,* where the English translations (or, when appropriate, the English originals) of the various writings are located. When citing any of Bacon's writings, I shall normally indicate the name of the piece and simply give a page-reference to the *Works,* or to Farrington (1964). With the *De Augmentis,* which is divided into books and chapters, I shall also indicate the part of the work to which I am referring. Since the *Novum Organum* is widely available in a number of editions and since it is, for the most part, divided into short aphorisms, I will simply cite the aphorism without giving any page-reference. *In Praise of Knowledge* appears in volume I of Spedding's (1862–74), 123–6.

The General Character of Bacon's Philosophy

Bacon was not a metaphysical philosopher in the traditional sense; he concerned himself very little with the nature of the soul, the meaning of necessity, or the essence of God. The driving force of Bacon's philosophy was his alarm at the lack of progress that could be discerned, since ancient times, in so many branches of science. Ancient learning, though it enjoyed a high reputation, seemed to Bacon to exhibit, for the most part, the shallowest understanding dressed up by various rhetorical devices, so that it acquired a mere show of profundity. That genuine understanding had not been achieved was evident to Bacon from the fact that no practical benefits had ever flowed from the established principles of natural philosophy. The wisdom of the Greeks, he said in the preface to the *Great Instauration*, "has the characteristic property of boys: it can talk, but it cannot generate; for it is fruitful of controversies but barren of works" (*Works* IV, 14). Bacon thought that the same sterility also afflicted some more modern sciences, such as alchemy.

> Are we the richer by one poor invention, by reason of all the learning that hath been this many hundred years? The industry of artificers maketh some small improvement of things invented; and chance sometimes in experimenting maketh us to stumble upon somewhat which is new: but all the disputation of the learned never brought to light one effect of nature before unknown. *(In Praise of Knowledge)*

The failure, as Bacon judged, of most of the physical inquiries that had so far been undertaken could not be blamed on any inferiority of intellect amongst earlier philosophers. In Bacon's view, the trouble lay in the methods by which they arrived at, and confirmed, their general hypotheses. Bacon considered that most physical inquiries had proceeded by one of two different ways, both of which he condemned. Some of them altogether ignored observations and experiments in formulating and supporting their conclusions, trusting instead in "the giddy whirl of argument". Others relied exclusively on experience, though of a restricted and trivial sort. Bacon's aim was to open up "a middle way between practical experience and unsupported theorising" (RP, 120).

The exact nature of the middle way that Bacon proposed will be the subject of the following chapters. As we shall see, the project of trying to understand Bacon cannot be entirely free from controversy, for he did not set out the principles of his approach with sufficient clarity for all the questions one would like to put to him to be answered with ease and assurance. Instead, one must look at the author's more or less indirect pronouncements and try to extract principles from the applications to which he put his method; the circumstantial nature of this evidence is bound to make one's conclusions somewhat uncertain. But this is not to say that every reading has an equal claim, and I shall argue in this book that one interpretation in particular is to be preferred above others.

An interpretation of Bacon's method that has been very widely favoured was advocated, in particular, by Robert Ellis, and more recently by Mary Hesse, who has spelled it out in greater detail. Their studies of Bacon's philosophy are amongst the clearest and most scholarly available, and so have proved extremely influential. I shall call the Ellis-Hesse interpretation the 'infallible-mechanical interpretation', to indicate its principal assumptions, namely that Bacon's method proceeds mechanically, to an infallible end. I shall take the liberty of also calling it the 'standard interpretation'. This will be convenient for the exposition and is certainly not meant to imply that it enjoys universal acceptance; nevertheless, it is true to say that that interpretation, or some variant of it, is very widely adopted. *My primary purpose is not, however, to criticize any particular interpretation, but to set out what I see as the principles of Bacon's philosophy and to present them as a coherent and unified methodology.*

A somewhat disappointing aspect of the infallible-mechanical interpretation is that, if correct, it does not speak well for either the depth of understanding or the acumen of a man who, in his own time and long after, was celebrated as a great and illustrious philosopher of science. For while some points about his method, as it emerges from that interpretation, are good and original, these qualities seldom appear together.

In Chapter One, I shall give an account of the standard interpretation; then in Chapter Two I shall set out an alternative interpretation which, I shall argue, accords much more closely with Bacon's own intentions and has the incidental attraction of removing some of the more blatant errors often attributed to him. As I see it, his scientific method, which I call the 'hypothetico-inductive method', is both good *and* original, in many more ways than is generally allowed.

A number of aspects of the present interpretation of Bacon's philosophy have already been pointed out by others, notably by Paolo Rossi, who has stressed the anti-dogmatism of his approach; by Mary Horton, who has carefully documented the many modern and sensible principles of Baconian experimentation; by Hesse and C. J. Ducasse, who have pointed out the "method of hypothesis" in Bacon's work; and by Adolf Grünbaum, who has successfully defended some of Bacon's inductive ideas against recent critics. However, it is often maintained (for example by Hesse) that a distinction needs to be drawn between Bacon's *ideal* method of science, with its utopian ambition to reach infallible, and mechanically generated, truths, which Bacon came to realize was flawed, and the principles that he eventually settled on, when the difficulties inherent in the ideal became apparent. The correct ideas that commentators find in Bacon's work are then usually regarded as belonging to the second category, of sub-ideal principles. I shall argue against the existence of such a distinction, and try to show that Bacon's various insights were part of a unified philosophy of science, which he maintained throughout, and which informed his discussion of most of the topics with which he dealt. In particular, I shall, in succeeding chapters, expound the characteristic portions of Bacon's scientific philosophy— concerning the interpretation and anticipation of nature, the aims of science, the idols, the state of contemporary science, and the role of experiment—in the light of alternative interpretations.

Chapter One
The Standard Interpretation

*For in anything which is well
set down, I am in good hope
that if the first reading move a
scruple or objection, the second
reading will of itself make an
answer.* (DA 9i, 119)

1(i) The Infallible-Mechanical Thesis

The scientific method attributed to Bacon by the standard
interpretation starts out with a mass of factual data, either casually
observed, or consciously sought by means of experiments, and
from these, by employing a set of simple rules which practically
anyone could operate, it builds up a complete body of knowledge,
which is both certain and infallibly true; the whole process is
virtually automatic and relies on no mysterious insights or flashes
of inspiration. These are the crucial aspects of the standard
interpretation, which determine its general character. As Ellis
(1857a, 23–4) put it,

> Absolute certainty, and a mechanical mode of procedure such
> that all men should be capable of employing it, are . . . two

great features of the Baconian method. His system can never
be rightly understood if they are neglected . . .

In due course, I shall dispute that either of these features
formed a part of Bacon's approach. But it is fair to say that there is
evidence in his writings which suggests that they did. For
instance, the idea that his method of discovery would necessarily
and infallibly produce the truth may seem to be behind Bacon's
invitation to his readers, in the preface to the *Novum Organum*,
to join him in seeking "not pretty and probable conjectures, but
certain and demonstrable knowledge" and in finding a way into
the "inner chambers" of nature. (*Works* IV, 42) And he claimed
that his method will "open and lay out a new and *certain* path for
the mind to proceed in" (*Works* IV, 40; my italics) and "performs
everything by the *surest rules and demonstrations*" (NO I, cxxii;
my italics). What could Bacon have meant other than that those
rules of procedure should be infallible? In the next chapter, I shall
suggest what else he meant.

Bacon also likened his method to a kind of mechanical engine
of discovery, fuelled by experiment and observation and needing
no special skill to operate. For instance, he compared discovery in
science by his method with the drawing of a perfect circle by
means of a compass for, unlike a free-hand construction, it "leaves
but little to the acuteness and strength of wits, but places all wits
and understandings nearly on a level." (NO I, lxi) He also declared
that while he had "provided the machine", "the stuff must be
gathered from the facts of nature". (Epistle Dedicatory to the
Great Instauration, Works IV, 12) And in the preface to the
Novum Organum, Bacon advised that the mind should "not [be]
left to take its own course, but [should be] guided at every step;
and the business be done as if by machinery." (*Works* IV, 40)

In order to meet the requirements of infallibility and machine-
like efficiency, the standard interpretation begins with the
assumption that, for Bacon, nature is in some sense finite and that
every possibility as to the true explanation of a particular
phenomenon can be surveyed in advance; induction is then the
technique whereby all accounts but the true one are excluded.

The particular assumption attributing finiteness to nature, or the "principle of limited variety", as it is sometimes called, which the standard interpretation employs, is the following: it is that the world is composed of a large number of "concrete" or "compound" bodies, such as lions and gold, each of which can be analysed into a finite number of "simple natures", or properties. The main evidence that Bacon held this view is usually drawn from his famous investigation into the nature of heat, which we shall examine in detail in Chapter Six. Bacon appears to give expression to the idea when, for instance, he described, with apparent approval, the view that

> regards a body as a troop or collection of simple natures. In gold, for example, the following properties meet. It is yellow in colour; heavy up to a certain weight; malleable or ductile to a certain degree of extension; it is not volatile, and loses none of its substance by the action of fire; it turns into liquid with a certain degree of fluidity; it is separated and dissolved by particular means; and so on for the other natures which meet in gold. (NO II, v)

The standard interpretation also has a definite view of the *aim* of Baconian science. While Bacon explained unambiguously that scientific understanding is achieved with the discovery of what he called *forms*, it is not so easy to determine exactly what he meant by this term. Hesse suggests that, for the method to work, the form of a given nature must be some other simple nature which always accompanies it in any body and is always accompanied by it. Suppose, for example, that we wish to discover the form of the simple nature S_{17}. The Baconian method, on this interpretation, requires one to select a compound body containing S_{17} and to enumerate all its other natures. Suppose that such a compound possesses the natures S_1, S_4, and S_{17}. The form of S_{17} is then either S_1 or S_4, and exactly which it is may be established by finding another compound exhibiting either S_{17} and S_4 but not S_1, or S_{17} and S_1 but not S_4. If the first of these is discovered, then S_4 is the form of S_{17}; if the latter, then it must be S_1. This will constitute, in Bacon's terminology, a "crucial" experiment. For the method always to lead to the true form, it is necessary to assume that the appropriate compounds comprise a finite number of simple natures. Secondly, this number must be fairly small, for otherwise the method could not be operated in practice. Thirdly, one must be able to enumerate each of these natures, at least in those compounds which need to be employed in the induction. And finally, it must be assumed that the appropriate compounds exist naturally and are always accessible, or else that they can be artificially created at will by experiment.

A number of topics discussed by Bacon are typically enlisted to reinforce this way of understanding his inductive method. For instance, he contrasted his own method, which he called the "interpretation of nature", with an unscientific approach in which nature is "anticipated". Anticipations are normally portrayed as speculative hypotheses, and they are distinguished from those theories that are infallibly demonstrated from the facts of nature in a process of interpretation. Secondly, Bacon's criticisms of the science of his day are frequently understood to have been directed against its unproven, hypothetical, or speculative character. Bacon also argued that certain attitudes of mind—he called them "idols"—encourage bad science and, in keeping with the above account, these are often assumed to be prejudices of various kinds in which speculative hypotheses are preferred over proven and infallible theories. The foundation, as it were, for Baconian science is observation and experiment, and he bestowed immense labour on describing and illustrating how such collections of facts, or "histories", should be compiled. A standard interpretation is that, for Bacon, these histories must betray no theoretical presuppositions at all, and should consist of 'pure' facts, infallibly drawn from 'direct' observation, so that they may then lead with the assurance of a logical deduction to general theories.

1(ii) How Good is Bacon's Method, According to its Standard Interpretation?

The method described by Ellis and Hesse bears little resemblance to modern and, one assumes, more correct ideas of the way that science is supposed to work. To be sure, the importance it accords to observation and experiment, and the role these play in knocking out possible forms of a given nature, in a kind of trial and error process, are broadly right. No doubt many natural philosophers of the time needed to be re-alerted to these rules of science, and certainly they have rarely received so eloquent an exposition. It has to be said, however, that they were not altogether original to Bacon. But the lack of originality in the worthwhile part of his method, as it is reported in the standard interpretation, is, unfortunately, a minor flaw compared with the shortcomings of the rest.

First of all, it permits no distinction between a form and a nature. If S_1 is the form of S_2, so is S_2 of S_1. Hence one could not interpret the form as the cause of a nature, at least not in any sense recognisable to modern science. (Bacon's theory of forms and his views on the types of cause that science should encompass are discussed in more detail in Chapter Three.) Secondly, the method attributed to Bacon considers scientific understanding to be obtained solely by correlating simple, directly observable, natures. I do not wish to suggest that such correlations, if discovered, would be useless; far from it. For example, the finding that a pendulum's length is correlated with its period, according to the well-known formula, was not an insignificant contribution to knowledge. But, since the seventeenth century, a more highly prized sort of discovery would locate the causes of observable phenomena in the deeper structures of bodies, in terms, say, of fields or of elementary particles of matter, and these cannot be perceived, at least not in the same direct way that yellowness or weight can be. By restricting science to surface phenomena for the sake of preserving its absolute certainty and avoiding any element of speculation, Bacon would appear to have had a conception of scientific explanation which has not been borne out by subsequent developments.

A more implausible element in Bacon's method, as it is described above, is its presumption that one could enumerate all the simple natures in a body. This was required in order to ensure that the copresence of two natures was indicative of a form-nature

Francis Bacon to students of literature and rhetoric. My view, however, is that Bacon's contribution to the understanding of scientific method is greatly undervalued by the scheme outlined above and that, properly understood, it is interesting, largely original and, as far as it goes, substantially correct. This is the point of view I shall explain and defend in this book.

Chapter Two
Bacon's Principles of Induction

*How good a thing to have the
motion of the mind concentric
with the universe!* (DA 6iii, 482)

2(i) Introduction

At the beginning of the *Novum Organum*, Bacon declared that
two kinds of induction exist, both starting out "from the senses
and particulars" and both ending in "the highest generalities" (NO
I xxii). He called one of these methods the "anticipation of
nature", the other the "interpretation of nature". The first, in
Bacon's view, was responsible for what he saw as the sterile and
unproductive character of much contemporary science, while he
argued for the second as the right procedure to adopt if science
was to make any substantial and more rapid advance. As I have
mentioned, according to a widely received opinion, Bacon held
that the interpretative method would in the end achieve sure and
certain theories, infallibly proved by infallible observations, while

on the other hand, the method of anticipation could produce only undemonstrated speculations or hypotheses: "Bacon's term 'anticipation' . . . means almost the same as 'hypothesis' (in my way of using this term)", we are told by Popper (1959, 279). Indeed, the equation of Bacon's method of anticipation with hypothetical reasoning is one that is frequently made:

> [Bacon] protested altogether against "anticipating nature," that is, forming our own hypotheses and theories as to what the laws of nature probably are, and he seemed to think that systematic arrangement of facts could take the place of all other methods. (Jevons, 1909, 255)

> The "hypothesis" of Kepler, the "mente concipio" of Galileo, Bacon must, on the basis of his central view, count among the "false anticipations" which afflict the human spirit and hinder it from pursuing the one sure and fruitful path of experience. Instead of such anticipations, such theoretical assumptions, and basic assumptions, he would substitute the interpretation of nature which can be derived only from a comparison of the given. (Cassirer, 1953, 47)

> He thought nature could be studied by rule, without the aid of hypotheses and scientific imagination. (Cajori, 1929, 55)

Bacon's soundness as a philosopher has often been questioned because of his alleged failure to see that the hypothetical method is part of the essential character of science, and not a disease to be remedied. For instance, M. R. Cohen described "Those [like Bacon] who think they can start any natural inquiry without 'anticipating nature' or making any assumptions at all" as "just complacently ignorant" (1949, 104). This is, perhaps, a surprising claim to make about a celebrated philosopher and, as I hope to show, it is quite mistaken.

2(ii) The Anticipation and Interpretation of Nature

The anticipation of nature, which Bacon also called the "old" or "common" logic, had a number of features which he held to account for the inertia and poverty of science. One of these was exhibited in the then accepted axioms, of which Bacon said that

> having been suggested by a scanty and manipular experience
> and a few particulars of most general occurrence, [they] are
> made for the most part just large enough to fit and take
> these in: and therefore it is no wonder if they do not lead to
> new particulars. And if some opposite instance, not observed
> or not known before, chance to come in the way, the axiom
> is rescued and preserved by some frivolous distinction;
> whereas the truer course would be to correct the axiom itself.
> (NO I, xxv)

The first thing to notice is that these remarks against the method of anticipation do not charge it with permitting an illegitimate intrusion of speculation into science. On the contrary, the criticism starts with the point that some theories that anticipate nature are *not* speculative, for they assert nothing more than the facts or observations which prompted their formulation. Bacon made the same point several times, for example when criticizing the tendency displayed in the established sciences to play safe, as it were, insofar as "they seize on experiments and effects already known and do no more than hold them together by a flimsy network of logic cut to the precise measure of the familiar facts." Bacon then objected, quite rightly, that "This does not amount to the demonstration of some causal relation or some natural process opening the way to effects and experiments as yet unknown" (TC, 86). And, in a similar vein:

> the sciences we now possess are merely systems for the nice
> ordering and setting forth of things already invented; not
> methods of invention or directions for new works. (NO I, viii)

However, as we saw, Bacon held that the tendency in the sciences merely to recapitulate the already known evidence was manifested only "for the most part" (NO I, xxv). He acknowledged that theories sometimes did extend beyond the given particulars and lead to new ones. Unfortunately though, the way of anticipation, when such predictions were not borne out in fact, was not to "correct the axiom itself", which Bacon said would be the "truer course", but rather to rescue and preserve it by "some frivolous distinction", the nature of which we shall consider shortly.

These deficiencies in the method of anticipation, or the old logic, are matched by corresponding merits in the new or "true logic", also called the "interpretation of nature". That is to say, theories which are interpretations must encompass more particulars than those which they were originally designed to explain and, secondly, some of those new particulars should be verified. This is how Bacon put it:

> in establishing axioms by this kind of induction [i.e., interpretation], we must also examine and try whether the axiom so established be framed to the measure of those particulars only from which it is derived, or whether it be larger and wider. (NO I, cvi)

As we have seen, the first of these disjuncts describes a defect of the method of anticipation, which therefore ought to be shunned. Interpretation must clearly respect the second condition; that is to say, its theories must be larger and wider than the facts from which they are drawn. However, an axiom that interprets nature should meet a further requirement. Bacon continued:

> And if it be larger and wider, we must observe whether by indicating to us new particulars it confirm that wideness and largeness as by a collateral security; that we may not either stick fast in things already known, or loosely grasp at shadows and abstract forms; not at things solid and realised in matter. (NO I, cvi)

In other words, as well as asserting more than the particulars it was originally designed to explain, an axiom should lead to new particulars, by predicting phenomena which are then verified in observation. In this way, an axiom will "confirm . . . as by a collateral security" the part of it which exceeded the original data.

Another tendency in anticipations is to confine theoretical interest to superficial phenomena, whence "The discoveries which have hitherto been made in the sciences are such as lie close to vulgar notions, scarcely beneath the surface" (NO I, xviii).

Elsewhere, Bacon berated those sciences that "appeal only to the familiar and the obvious, in which the human mind contentedly acquiesces, but make no effort to get beneath the surface of nature" (TC, 86). The best sciences, by contrast, investigate the physical causes of phenomena, and these must be sought in the minute particles of matter:

> For seeing that every natural action depends on things
> infinitely small, or at least too small to strike the sense, no
> one can hope to govern or change nature until he has duly
> comprehended and considered *(notaverit)* them. (NO II, vi)*

The two notable worked examples of an interpretation of nature which Bacon presented, concerning colour and heat, do both fulfil this requirement, by locating those phenomena in the smaller, and evidently invisible, particles of matter. We shall examine the details of these examples in later chapters.

One other type of reasoning that Bacon associated with the anticipation of nature is induction by simple enumeration, which he hastily condemned as "a puerile thing; [that] concludes at hazard; is always liable to be upset by a contradictory instance; takes into account only what is known and ordinary; and leads to no result" *(Plan,* 25). Bacon took no trouble to explain exactly what he took simple enumeration to be, though he was presumably referring to the kind of induction which just generalises from observed instances. Jardine (1974, 23) discovered the following example of traditional induction in a textbook of logic of 1539:

> Adam, a blessed and pious man, had a cross to bear; So did
> Abel; So did Abraham; So did Jacob; So did Christ; nor are
> dissimilar cases to be found. Therefore all blessed and pious
> men have a cross to bear.

This is, indeed, a rather puerile example, though not necessarily of a puerile pattern of reasoning, as we all pursue a

---

*The Spedding translation renders *notaverit* as *observed,* which would make Bacon's thought contradictory. The word is more accurately given in English as 'took notice of', or 'marked', or 'considered'.

somewhat similar cognitive course in arriving at low-level generalisations. Bacon's antipathy to simple enumeration as the universal method of science derived, first of all, from his preference for theories that deal with interior physical causes, which are not immediately observable. Simple enumeration cannot do this, for it generalises only upon what is "known and ordinary". Secondly, Bacon argued that "to conclude upon a bare enumeration of particulars (as the logicians do) without instance contradictory, is a vicious conclusion", and can produce no more than a "probable conjecture", whereas Bacon aspired to certainty by a process of testing and excluding false conjectures (DA 5ii, 410). We shall examine Bacon's notion of a probable conjecture a few sections hence.

Bacon did not deny that those who proceed by anticipation may sometimes stumble upon an important novelty, like gunpowder, but these are isolated instances: "A pig might print the letter A with its snout in the mud, but you would not on that account expect it to go on to compose a tragedy." It is similar with the occasional successes of anticipation. If these had been governed "not by good luck but by good guidance", they would not have stood alone but would have been accompanied by a "host of noble inventions of a kindred sort" (MBT, 71).

In general, then, it appears that anticipating nature is a highly conservative method, whose theories either just cover, or recapitulate, the data, or else, once advanced, are rigidly protected from alteration or replacement, however unfavourable the evidence. And, in keeping with this conservatism, the theories produced by the method of anticipation are inclined to deal just with surface phenomena, rather than with underlying physical causes.

2(iii) The Anticipation of Nature and Conventionalism

The anticipation of nature is similar in several respects worth noting to a philosophy of science often called 'conventionalism' or 'instrumentalism', which was popular, especially in astronomy, in Bacon's time, and which has also, incidentally, enjoyed renewed support more recently from such philosophers as Duhem, Mach, Wittgenstein, Ryle, and Hanson.

This methodology arose in the first instance in the context of astronomy, where theories were in danger of conflicting with certain well-entrenched views on the properties of matter. And it had also been deployed around Bacon's time in an effort to stem the controversy between the Copernican idea that the sun was stationary and the earth in motion, and the very different view which the Bible appeared to endorse. These potential controversies are nipped in the bud by conventionalism, not by straightforwardly banning the usual kind of theoretical explanations, but by imposing a particular interpretation upon them. To be more specific, conventionalists assert that theories apparently referring to unobservable entities, such as atoms and epicycles, should not be understood literally, for they are not in fact meaningful statements; they are, on the contrary, only 'computation rules' or, in Ryle's phrase, 'inference licences', whose role is merely to explain and predict particular kinds of *observable* events. (Alan Musgrave, 1980, gives the best recent account and critique of the philosophy of conventionalism.)

As we shall see later, Bacon certainly took conventionalism as his main adversary when discussing astronomy, and since that methodology condones several practices which Bacon explicitly contested, it is likely that it was also a target in his more general campaign against the established methods of science.

First of all, conventionalism does not countenance speculation on unobservables, and this was a weakness that Bacon discerned in the old logic. Secondly, conventionalism, like anticipation, allows the kind of 'frivolous distinction', or 'ad hoc adjustment' as it is now more usually called, which Bacon condemned. This comes about because, according to the conventionalist, theories containing apparent reference to entities with which we could have no direct acquaintance are really rules, or instruments, for analysing and organising observable phenomena and are not meaningful statements at all; hence, the categories of 'true' and 'false' and 'likely' do not apply to them. Therefore, it is needless for such theories to appear plausible, for their role is not to describe convincingly but simply to save the phenomena, to use an ancient expression traditionally applied in this context. As Duhem (1908, 92) put it, "Astronomical hypotheses are simply devices for saving the phenomena; provided they serve this end, they need not be true nor even likely." So, if a theory, treated as a convention, produces a false prediction, it is perfectly in order to hedge it about with an appropriate restriction or to vary some auxiliary assumption, with a view simply to restoring consistency between fact and theory, without regard to the plausibility or reasonableness of the revised explanation. Thus, Bacon described the various hypotheses of astronomers as "the speculations of one who cares not what fictions he introduces into nature, provided his calculations answer" (DIG, 517). And alchemists too, Bacon found, would uphold their hermetic principles, come what may, by similar devices:

> For the Alchemist nurses eternal hope, and when the thing fails, lays the blame upon some error of his own; fearing either that he has not sufficiently understood the words of his art or of his authors (whereupon he turns to tradition and auricular whispers), or else that in his manipulations he has made some slip of a scruple in weight or a moment in time (whereupon he repeats his trials to infinity) . . . (NO I, lxxxv)

Karl Popper, whose philosophy, as we shall see, possesses more than a passing resemblance to Bacon's, also identified the conventionalist approach to science as an obstacle to further development because it permits an unbridled use of ad hoc adjustments in order to defend the established theories; indeed, he did this in almost the same terms as Bacon:

> Whenever the 'classical' system of the day is threatened by the results of new experiments which might be interpreted as falsifications according to my point of view, the system will appear unshaken to the conventionalist. He will explain away the inconsistencies which may have arisen; perhaps by

blaming our inadequate mastery of the system. Or he will eliminate them by suggesting *ad hoc* the adoption of certain auxiliary hypotheses, or perhaps of certain corrections to our measuring instruments. (1959, 80)

2(iv) The Role of Hypotheses

The faults which Bacon identified in the established methods of investigation do not appear, at least from the foregoing, to include an employment of hypotheses. Indeed, a primary defect of anticipation, in Bacon's estimation, is its reluctance to speculate, particularly in regard to things not immediately observable. By the same token, the interpretation of nature requires theories to be hypothetical, at any rate at the outset, in the sense that they are expected to go beyond the original evidence and then be confirmed through new predictions. As Bacon put it elsewhere,

> the true method of experience . . . first lights the candle, and then by means of the candle shows the way; commencing as it does with experience duly ordered and digested, not bungling or erratic, and from it educing axioms, and from established axioms again new experiments . . . (NO I, lxxxii)

Nevertheless, it is an entrenched opinion that Bacon opposed those sciences whose conclusions went beyond the data, or what could logically be deduced from them, whose conclusions were, in that sense, hypothetical. As I indicated earlier, in the first section of this chapter, Bacon's anticipation of nature has frequently been identified with a hypothetical method. One further illustration of this point of view comes from Popper, who claimed that the method rejected by Bacon "is in fact a method of interpretation, in the modern sense of the word. It is the *method of conjecture or hypothesis* (a method of which, incidentally, I happen to be a convinced advocate)" (1963, 14).

A number of philosophers, such as Ducasse and Hesse, on the other hand, do concede that Bacon accorded an important role to hypotheses, though only when he was forced to do so after realizing that the ideal method he was proposing could not work. And some commentators discern two levels in Bacon's projected science, only one of which would allow hypotheses: "Bacon's position is not that we are to cease making hypotheses. We may make them and use them, but we are not to admit them to the body of science." (Storck, 1931, 178)

My own view, on the other hand, is that Bacon welcomed hypotheses (in the sense of theories going beyond what is immediately given in perception) from the very beginning, and that they were always the intended product of the interpretative method. This view is supported, first of all, by Bacon's criticism of the method of anticipation for failing to reach beneath the surfaces of phenomena. (These criticisms show, incidentally, that Popper could not have been further from the truth when he characterised Baconian anticipation as being "an attempt to interpret what is manifest in nature in the light of non-manifest causes or of hypotheses" (1963, 14). Indeed the inability of the established methods of science to discover those "non-manifest causes" was one of the chief defects which interpretations were designed to combat.) Secondly, as we have seen, Bacon explicitly required those axioms which interpret nature to go beyond the original data, so that they are bound to be hypothetical, or speculative, to some degree.

One reason why speculation often seems to be the enemy in Bacon's drive against the method of anticipation lies in the many occasions where he faulted it apparently because it "flies from the senses and particulars to the most general axioms" (NO I, xix), and because it encourages the mind's longing "to spring up to positions of higher generality" (NO I, xx). "The understanding must not," Bacon said, "be allowed to jump and fly from particulars to remote axioms and [ones] of almost the highest generality" (NO I, civ).

These remarks, taken together with the earlier ones on the interpretation of nature, seem to imply that Bacon had incompatible requirements for his favoured method of science. On the one hand, the new axioms must be larger and wider than the particulars from which they are drawn and, on the other, the interpreter of nature should beware of flying to remote axioms. However, an examination of the context of the above quotations resolves the seeming conflict and shows Bacon's chief target to have been not speculation itself, but the dogmatic defence of speculations and the tendency to regard them as infallible or unalterable. Thus, the quotations restored to their contexts read as follows:

> [Anticipation of nature] flies from the senses and particulars to the most general axioms, and from these principles, *the truth of which it takes for settled and immoveable*, proceeds to judgment and to the discovery of middle axioms. (NO I, xix; my italics)

> For the mind longs to spring up to positions of higher generality, *that it might find rest there; and so after a little while wearies of experiment*. (NO I, xx; my italics)

Bacon made the same point in practically every one of the many places where he warned against the mind's taking flight to very general axioms, namely, that the danger resides in their being mistaken for unshakable truths:

> [The ancients] started from worthless inductions and jumped at once to conclusions of the highest generality. *These they took as the poles on which their world of discourse revolved; everything else they adapted to conform with these fixed and changeless truths.* (RP, 129–30; my italics)

And similarly,

> The understanding must not however be allowed to jump and fly from particulars to remote axioms and [ones] of almost the highest generality (such as the first principles, as they are called, of arts and things), *and taking stand upon them as truths that cannot be shaken*, proceed to prove and frame the middle axioms by reference to them . . . (NO I, civ; my italics)

> For hitherto the proceeding has been to fly at once from the
> sense and particulars up to the most general propositions, *as
> certain fixed poles* for the argument to turn upon . . . (*Plan,*
> 25; my italics)

> From a few examples and particulars . . . they [the ancients]
> flew at once to the most general conclusions, or first
> principles of science: *taking the truth of these as fixed and
> immoveable,* they proceeded by means of intermediate
> propositions to educe and prove from them the inferior
> conclusions; and out of these they framed the art. (NO I,
> cxxv; my italics)

The immediate continuation of the last quotation reveals the link
in Bacon's mind between his precept against flying to generalities
and his criticism of the dogmatic method of anticipation, for he
said,

> After that, if any new particulars and examples repugnant to
> their dogmas were mooted and adduced, either they subtly
> moulded them into their system by distinctions or
> explanations of their rules, or else coursely got rid of them by
> exceptions; while to such particulars as were not repugnant
> they laboured to assign causes in conformity with those their
> principles. (NO I, cxxv)

Bacon's primary object in these remarks on speculation was,
then, to criticize those natural philosophers who adopt
hypotheses, particularly ones of the highest generality, on the
basis of a "few examples and particulars", and then act as if they
were certainly true and beyond revision. Such philosophers are
then reluctant to examine the hypotheses further ("the mind . . .
wearies of experiment") and, if any new evidence should appear
which would tell against a hypothesis, they turn it aside by the
device which Bacon called a 'distinction' and which, as we have
seen, he elsewhere condemned as "frivolous". No doubt, a further
message may be drawn, namely that speculation is to be frowned
on if it is *excessive and precipitate,* as when it results from flying
"at once" to the most general conclusions. I shall defer a
discussion of this aspect to pages 52–56.

2(v) Epicurus on Anticipation

It is, perhaps, worth observing at this point that the most probable pedigree of Bacon's concept of anticipations is also inimical to their being read as hypotheses and, in fact, it favours the present view that they were conventions, immune from revision by empirical means. For Bacon's idea of an anticipation seems to owe a good deal to the Epicurean doctrine of the same name. Certainly, Bacon was well-acquainted with Epicurean ideas, for he referred to Epicurus directly on a number of occasions. An 'anticipation', in the philosophy of Epicurus, was the kind of thing that Bishop Berkeley later argued was impossible, namely, a general idea, which manifests itself in the form of a clear mental image. The image is created out of frequently repeated sense-perceptions, for example of different horses, which operate to produce a picture, as it were, incorporating only the common elements of those perceptions. As Diogenes Laertius (c. 200 AD) related, once "stored in the mind", this picture, or anticipation, acts as an organising principle and as one of the "standards of truth" (Hicks, 1925, II, 563 and 163). The mind employs anticipations in these roles by matching incoming perceptions with the preconceived pattern given by the anticipation, a procedure which allows it to determine to which category the object in view belongs; whether it is a horse or a man, say. Epicurean anticipations share with Baconian anticipations (as I understand them) the characteristics that they derive from sense perception; that, once formed, they become fixed and unalterable; and that they then operate as conventions, or rules, for organising observations. Bacon's view was, of course, different in many ways from that of Epicurus: he certainly did not think of anticipations as clear mental images, and he also added many details completely absent from any account we have from Epicurus.

Before drawing a tentative conclusion from the similarity between Bacon and Epicurus, I must justify the slight oversimplification of saying that the two doctrines went under the same name, for, of course, the original sources for the work of Epicurus are in Greek, where the clear mental images I

mentioned earlier were called *prolepses*. However, in Bacon's
time, the most widely available accounts of the theory were in
Latin, and the most favoured translation of *prolepsis* seems to
have been *anticipatio*. Lucretius was an exception, for he used the
word *notities*, but his account of this part of Epicurus' theory was
very sketchy, and limited to two brief and widely separated
sections, one of four lines and the other of three. The fullest
exposition, and the one which would probably have made the
greatest impact, appears in the book *Lives of Eminent
Philosophers,* by Diogenes Laertius, where the theory receives a
very much more substantial and detailed treatment. All the Latin
translations of this work which were available to Bacon used
anticipatio as the word for Epicurus' mental images. Although
Bacon had some Greek, he would have been much more at home
in and adept at Latin and would, most likely, have studied
Diogenes Laertius in that language. Moreover, of the editions of
the *Lives* available to Bacon, only one, that of 1533, presented the
Greek text by itself; all the others contained Latin translations,
though a few of these were accompanied by the Greek original.
What appears to be Bacon's own copy of the *Lives* is preserved at
the Francis Bacon Library. It is in a Latin translation of 1596.

If Bacon had intended anticipations merely as hypotheses or
speculations, there are many familiar words he could have
employed, and the fact that he copied an established technical
term is surely significant, for he is unlikely to have done this
without intending some apt allusion to the doctrine to which the
term originally referred. Since the central features of that doctrine
bear a marked resemblance to the account I have given of Bacon's
theory, I take this fact as giving some indication of the accuracy of
that account.

2(vi) Certainty and Bacon's Method

2(vi a) The Infallibility Thesis.   Another reason why Bacon's
method has acquired a reputation for being antipathetic to

hypotheses is its supposed goal of infallibility. Since hypotheses say more than is given in observation, they are necessarily not infallible and hence, it is inferred, they can have no role to play in the Great Instauration.

Now the infallibility thesis has been read into Bacon's work principally on the basis of remarks to the effect that theories can, with sufficient support from the facts, be 'demonstrated' or 'established' and thereby made 'certain', all of which has bred the belief that the Baconian method aimed at the certainty of infallibility. This is an interpretation which I shall try to refute. First of all, some statements of that view:

> [Bacon] aimed at giving a wholly new method,—a method universally applicable, and in all cases infallible. (Ellis, 1857a, 24)

> Bacon's faith in the infallibility of the method seems to rest on four assumptions. (Hesse, 1964, 145)

> Bacon undertook to give an infallible rule by which any one could, with perseverance, make scientific discoveries. (Cajori, 1929, 55)

Bacon has been much criticized for, supposedly, claiming an "absolute immunity from error" (Ellis, 1857a, 24) for his method, since this implies that the only good scientific theories are either empty truisms or else collections of immediate impressions of the senses (if one could regard these as incorrigible), both of which alternatives would turn Baconian science into a truncated and impoverished enterprise, vastly different from science as actually practised. It is therefore imperative, if Bacon is to be rescued as a significant contributor to the philosophy of science, that his certainty claim be re-examined to see whether, as I think, a more modest and defensible gloss can be put on it.

2(vi b) On the Prospect of Proving the Principles of Induction.   One consideration which tells against the infallibility interpretation is the modesty of Bacon's defence of his inductive scheme. There is no possibility, he tells us, of its principles being conclusively proved, nor of rival systems being definitively refuted. Bacon came, as he picturesquely put it, as a "trumpeter, not a combatant" (DA 4i, 372) and, like the French when they entered Italy, "with chalk in their hands to mark out their lodgings, not with arms to force their way in". (NO I, xxxv) He likewise would have his doctrines "enter quietly" into minds which are prepared for it: "for confutations cannot be employed, when the difference is upon first principles and very notions and even upon forms of demonstration." (NO I, xxxv)

This is a reasonable point: any proof to establish or refute a particular "form of demonstration" itself requires some form of demonstration. But, as Bacon said, his own method cannot be judged by the standards of a rival method, such as those of anticipation, for he "cannot be called on to abide by the sentence of a tribunal which is itself on its trial" (NO I, xxxiii). The only alternative is for the method to be validated by its own method of demonstration. However, any such validation would be circular, as is illustrated, for example, by defenders of certain principles of induction who argue that a theory will be reliable in the future if it has been successful up till now, on the grounds that successful theories in the past have not let us down. Descartes got into a famous circle of this kind, when defending his truth-criterion of clarity and distinctness by appeal to principles whose certainty relied on the very criterion being defended. Baron Münchhausen might perhaps have tried to pull himself up by his own bootstraps, but Baron Verulam declined to make the attempt, evidently aware that it would be futile. It is not surprising then that Bacon did not urge his method with any arguments that pretended to be decisive, for he denied that there are any such arguments: "the refutation of these [received systems of philosophy] has been such, as alone it could be: that is to say, by signs and the evidence of causes" (NO I, cxv). The signs, which, in a manner of speaking, refute the rival systems of philosophy, are that the latter have resulted in repetitiousness, disputatiousness, and stagnation. But: "Of all signs there is none more certain or more noble than that taken from fruits. For fruits and works are as it were sponsors and sureties for the truth of philosophies." (NO I, lxxiii)

These fruits and works are simply the predictions of new particulars that should emerge in the interpretative process and it is evident that Bacon did not expect them to prove axioms, in the strong sense of somehow exhibiting their supposed infallibility; they are merely "signs", and obviously fallible ones, that the theory is true. He justified the search for such predictions on the same grounds but in slightly different terms, on several occasions. For instance, they are said to act as "collateral security" and as "pledges of truth", which "confirm" hypotheses; but Bacon never said that they establish hypotheses up to the hilt and with finality.

It is significant, too, that Bacon did not think that the interpretation of nature, in the form in which he had expounded it, was the last word in method, or was necessarily correct in all its details, as he made clear in the concluding words of the first book of the *Novum Organum:* "Nor again do I mean to say that no improvement can be made upon these [precepts]. On the contrary, I that regard the mind not only in its own faculties, but in its connection with things, must needs hold that the art of discovery may advance as discoveries advance." It is not surprising, then, that Bacon *commended* his new method of induction to his readers, but refused to *command* agreement by deploying arguments pretending to conclusiveness or finality, for he knew full well that no such argument would work. This, I think, undermines L. J. Cohen's claim (1980, 222) that Bacon mistakenly expected "that his method could even in the end produce conclusively certain results." It also blocks the accompanying explanation of that alleged mistake, which Cohen says "sprang from a failure to recognise that in eliminative induction every prior assumption about the variety of hypotheses that are open to elimination is itself empirically corrigible."

It seems to me very unlikely that Bacon made so glaring a blunder, especially in view of his objection to the sovereign position which the syllogism had usurped in scientific reasoning. This objection reveals that he well knew that the conclusion of a logical argument can be relied upon absolutely only if its premises have been established beyond any conceivable doubt. The syllogism, Bacon observed, "consists of propositions, propositions consist of words, words are symbols of notions. Therefore if the notions themselves (which is the root of the matter) are confused and over-hastily abstracted from the facts, there can be no firmness in the superstructure" (NO I, xiv). He then added, "Our only hope therefore lies in a true induction." It seems then either that Bacon overlooked the fact that by claiming infallibility he was hoist by his own petard, or else that he never held the infallibility thesis, which I believe is the case.

2(vi c) A Game-Theoretic Argument.   One other indication that Bacon did not rest the new method on the infallible-mechanical thesis is a game-theoretic argument which, in the manner of Pascal's wager, enjoins us to support the scientific endeavour on the grounds that we have nothing much to lose, but a great deal to gain. The argument proceeds as follows:

> even if the breath of hope which blows on us from that New Continent were fainter than it is and harder to perceive; yet the trial (if we would not bear a spirit altogether abject) must by all means be made. For there is no comparison between that which we may lose by not trying and by not succeeding; since by not trying we throw away the chance of an immense good; by not succeeding we only incur the loss of a little human labour. (NO I, cxiv)

The form of this argument can be depicted with a game-grid in which the two options of engaging or not engaging in research meet one of two outcomes, depending on whether knowledge is available by such means or not. Plusses and minuses stand for gains and losses, and a zero indicates some neutral state:

	Knowledge	
	Available	Not available
Research	+	−
No research	0	0

In view of the disbenefit of the wasted effort from researching to no effect, Bacon's argument cannot depend just on the dominance principle that since research would be advantageous, or at least not disadvantageous, whatever the outcome, it is the preferred strategy. The argument must instead assume that the chances are weighted in favour of success to a sufficient degree to compensate for the costs of failure. Indeed, this is just how Bacon did argue, for he referred to "the breath of hope which blows on us from that New Continent", and pointed out that this has more than enough strength to justify proceeding. This argument would surely be surplus to requirement and unlikely to have been offered if its author had conceived anything more powerful to establish the infallibility of his method, and the inevitability of progress through it.

2(vi d) Certainty as an Extreme Degree of Confidence.   However we judge Bacon's certainty claim in toto, it clearly encapsulates the truth to the extent that theories which are maximally supported by the evidence are very highly approved and command the greatest confidence from scientists; such theories are certain at least in that sense. That theories enjoy varying degrees of confidence, and sometimes very great confidence, is suggested, for one thing, by the fact that practical projects, whose failure would incur tremendous costs, are often designed on the assumption that such theories are true. Moreover, the greater a theory's inductive support, the more would be wagered on its reliability, thus suggesting that plausibility and inductive support are closely connected. This is also reflected in the terminology of scientists, both in our own day and in Bacon's, who frequently speak of theories as being 'proved', or 'established', or 'verified' by experiment. The precise meaning of such terms is perhaps not quite clear, but nobody, I take it, imagines that scientists are deceived into thinking that every theoretical possibility but one has been refuted, or that they believe the theory to which they are assenting is necessarily true. The use of those terms simply reflects the undoubted truth that people are often inclined to believe well-confirmed theories.

2(vi e) Ideas of Inductive Proof in Bacon's Time.   The idea that
evidence may 'prove' or 'demonstrate' a theory, without thereby
transforming it into a necessary truth, is not a quirk of today's
speech but was also taken for granted around the period Bacon
was living, such 'proofs' being best construed as the process
whereby favourable evidence gradually raises a theory's
acceptability or plausibility and sometimes makes it so difficult to
deny that it can be said to be 'certain'. I think this is all Bacon
meant by his claim to have a sure and certain method and I also
believe that, as L. J. Cohen (1980) has argued, his near
contemporaries would have understood him in this way too. For
instance, there is no sense of conclusiveness or finality in
Shakespeare's concepts of proof and demonstration, when he had
Iago refer to facts which "may help to thicken other proofs/That do
demonstrate thinly" (*Othello* III iii). Similarly, Sir Kenelm Digby,
discussing the loadstone (in 1644), referred to "experimental
proofs and observations . . . by which it will appear that these
causes are well esteemed and applied"—not "infallible", be it
noted. And William Harvey, writing at almost the same time as
Bacon, tells us that his theory that the blood circulates through
the body would be "further proved from certain consequences" of
that theory, consequences which "are not without their use *in
exciting belief*" (1628, 90; my italics). William Fulke, writing in
1560, though he also talked of proofs in the mathematical sense of
propositions being deduced from more general principles,
regarded scientific induction as a form of demonstration similar to
that which I believe can be ascribed to Bacon. The conclusions of
such demonstrations, he said, are not infallible or necessarily true
propositions; they are rather ones that "no man neede to doubt,
but that they are moste true and certain":

> this is common to all sciences, that they may bee
> demonstrated. For although the principles and grounds in
> every arte, be of suche nature, that they canne not bee
> shewed and confyrmed by things more general, and therfore
> it is said, that they cannot be proued, yet by demonstration

> or induction they maye be so playnly sette before our eies,
> that no man neede to doubte, but that they are moste true
> and certain. (1560, 15–16)

Finally, Joseph Glanvill, who was an excellent philosopher and a
well-versed Baconian, entirely supports the present interpretation
of Bacon's claim that theories may be demonstrated and rendered
certain by his method. He distinguished, in a very useful way,
between two senses of 'certainty':

> It is taken either (1.) for a firm assent to any thing, of which
> there is no reason of doubt; and this may be called
> *Indubitable* Certainty; or (2.) for an absolute Assurance, that
> things are as we conceive and affirm, and not possible to be
> otherwise, and this is *Infallible* Certainty. (1676, 47)

The second sort of certainty is one that *"humanely we cannot
attain unto, for it may not be absolutely impossible, but that our
faculties may be so contrived, as always to deceive us in the things
we judge most certain and assured"* (p. 50). And in practice a
"fullness of assent is all the certainty we have, or can pretend to"
(p. 49). This indeed is the kind of certainty which, in Glanvill's
view, Bacon hoped to achieve with his method:

> To propose their Opinions as *Hypothesis*, that *may probably*
> be the true accounts, without peremptorily affirming that
> *they are*. This, among others, hath been the way of those
> Great Men, the Lord *Bacon* and Des Cartes; and is now the
> method of the *Royal Society* of *London*. (p. 44)

Glanvill gave no hint that this interpretation of Bacon was
unusual, nor, so far as I am aware, did he excite any controversy
with it. Bacon does not seem to have conveyed the impression to
his immediate successors that his method would be infallible. Nor,
indeed, were other scientists who wrote with Baconian confidence
about the supposed reliability of their conclusions taken for
infallibilists: for instance, Gilbert, who claimed to infer the
diurnal motion of the earth "not with mere probability, but with
certainty" (1600, 327).

Bacon never intimated that he was applying an unusual connotation to terms when he claimed his method could prove and demonstrate axioms, and render them certain; it seems reasonable, therefore, to take his words literally, as saying that theories may be confirmed and gradually made more credible or probable by his method, eventually so probable as to be 'certain'.

2(vi f) Bacon's Opposition To Conjectures.   It might be said against this way of understanding Bacon that it is inconsistent with his critical remarks on conjectures. For, as we observed in Chapter One, Bacon contrasted the "certain and demonstrable knowledge" promised by his method with the "pretty and probable conjectures" which, he said, were the characteristic products from anticipating nature.

However, the appearance of a conflict is predicated upon a particular, indeed a peculiar, way of understanding the word 'conjecture'. Standard dictionaries inform us that a conjecture is "an opinion offered on insufficient presumptive evidence", a "guess" or "surmise", or an "unverified supposition". According to the *Oxford English Dictionary*, the word has carried these meanings since at least 1530. Certain philosophical circles, on the other hand, have recently invested the word with a further meaning, equating a conjecture with a speculation which goes beyond what is immediately given, on the supposition that such speculations are *necessarily* based on insufficient evidence. Popper, for example, whose influence here has been considerable, avers that the chief theories of science are so poorly supported by presumptive evidence that they all have zero probability, which means that they are all equally and maximally uncertain. This is a position he has repeatedly advanced on the basis of a variety of what Colin Howson (1973) has shown to be spurious 'proofs'. This is not the place to inquire into those alleged demonstrations or to examine the claims they were designed to establish. Suffice it to say that the 'philosophical' meaning of 'conjecture' is not one that is sanctioned by lexicographers, nor was it in vogue, even in philosophical circles, in Bacon's day.

Bacon, I think, took 'conjectures' in the dictionary sense to refer to doubtful guesses which have, as yet, insufficient support to be committed to the body of accepted ideas, but which nevertheless may be perfectly respectable preliminary theories for scientists to entertain, though in a tentative way. Indeed, Bacon himself published a number of such conjectures in the hope that they would eventually be "made good by experience." He thought that by making these conjectures public he would quench despondency in any of his readers who might doubt that scientific induction could achieve very much. As he said,

> it is fit that I publish and set forth those conjectures of mine which make hope in this matter reasonable; just as Columbus did, before that wonderful voyage of his across the Atlantic, when he gave the reasons for his conviction that new lands and continents might be discovered besides those which were known before; which reasons, though rejected at first, were afterwards made good by experience, and were the causes and beginnings of great events. (NO I, xcii)

Unless we take the making good by experience as some process which could, per impossibile, transform the original theory into an infallible truth—which I have argued was not Bacon's intention—we must admit that it will remain conjectural in the sense of going beyond the evidence, but may cease to be conjectural in the normal sense of that term.

I shall defer a detailed appraisal of Bacon's method to the next section, except for remarking that this conclusion seems reasonable enough. It does not bar speculation on hidden causes and processes from Baconian science, but it does allow those speculations to be confirmed and to acquire a high degree of certainty. Many modern physical theories—e.g., that water is composed of two atoms of hydrogen to every atom of oxygen— have these qualities.

It is worth noting as well, in relation to conjectures, that those which emanate from anticipating nature, besides being ill-founded, have an ensnaring and superficially pleasing quality. They are "pretty and probable", the second qualification almost certainly being used in what the *Oxford English Dictionary* describes as its "bad sense", to mean "specious". It perhaps also carried the sense of "commonplace," as when William Harvey seems to equate the "probable reasonings" by which the circulation of the blood is "further confirmed", and which are mentioned in the title of his Chapter 15 of the *De Motu Cordis*, with the "certain familiar reasonings", based on well-known and commonplace phenomena, that appear in the body of that chapter.

"Probable reasonings", as Bacon used the expression, also emerge from contemplating merely what is already known, without having recourse to new experiments. Thus he concluded his discussion of "Instances of the Fingerpost" (i.e., crucial experiments; see below, in Chapter Six), saying that he had "dwelt on them at some length, to the end that men may gradually learn and accustom themselves to judge of nature by Instances of the Fingerpost and Experiments of Light, and not by probable reasonings" (NO II, xxxvi). And finally, Bacon said of those who seek merely "pretty and probable conjectures" that they will be "content to rest in and use the knowledge *which has already been discovered*" (NO, preface; my italics).

It seems likely, then, that the pretty and probable conjectures produced when nature is anticipated earn their opprobrium not through being fallible, but in virtue of their uncertainty and lack of evidential support, especially from new experiments, coupled with a dangerous surface allure. Bacon touched on the speciousness of anticipations in the following:

> For the winning of assent, indeed, anticipations are far more powerful than interpretations; because being collected from a few instances, and those for the most part of familiar occurrence, they straightway touch the understanding and fill the imagination; whereas interpretations on the other hand, being gathered here and there from very various and widely dispersed facts, cannot suddenly strike the understanding; and therefore they must needs, in respect of the opinions of the time, seem harsh and out of tune; much as the mysteries of faith do. (NO I, xxviii)

2(vi g) Summary. I would summarise my view on Bacon's certainty claim in this way. He believed that theories should be advanced to explain whatever data were available in a particular domain. These theories should preferably concern the underlying physical, causal mechanisms and ought, in any case, to go beyond the data which generated them. They are then tested by drawing out new predictions, which, if verified in experience, may confirm the theory and may eventually render it certain, at least in the sense that it becomes very difficult to deny. The term 'moral certainty' has been coined by philosophers to refer to statements which, though not logical truths, have so impressive a claim to truth that belief in them is almost irresistible.

2(vii) Appraising Bacon's Method

2(vii a) The Interpretation of Nature and Falsificationism. If Bacon's contention that certainty could be achieved by his method is interpreted in the manner I have suggested, then his principles of induction take on a much more interesting and favourable appearance than would otherwise be the case. One aspect that I want to focus on is their similarity with what is often supposed, especially by its author, to be a diametrically opposed philosophy, namely falsificationism. Whilst it is true that there are notable divergences between the two philosophies, very striking similarities abound, which I think it will be fruitful to examine— not, however, in order to initiate a priority dispute, but to reinforce the particular interpretation of Bacon's philosophy that I am proposing. It will also be useful to note the differences between Popper's and Bacon's scientific methods, showing, as they do, that time and experience may not always lead to the improvement of a philosophy.

First, consider the similarities. Popper regarded scientific theories as hypothetical, partly because they deal with entities and processes lying beyond immediate perception and, as we have observed, the same reason committed Bacon, at least tacitly, to a similar view.

Next, like Bacon, Popper required that these theories go beyond the original data: "the new theory should be *independently testable*. That is to say, apart from explaining all the *explicanda* which the new theory was designed to explain, it must have new and testable consequences (preferably consequences of a *new kind*); it must lead to the prediction of phenomena which have not so far been observed" (1963, 241). Compare this requirement with Bacon's insistence that a theory should not be "framed to the measure of those particulars only from which it is derived," but should be "larger and wider".

Popper, however, noticed that indefinitely many hypotheses might satisfy this condition and, in an effort to discriminate between them, his revised philosophy introduced the further limitation that a theory should not only make new predictions, but that some of these should be verified. That a theory "should be successful in some of its new predictions" is what Popper called his "third requirement" (1963, 247). It corresponds to the Baconian injunction to observe "whether [an axiom] by indicating to us new particulars . . . confirm that wideness and largeness".

There are other similarities between Bacon and Popper. Both, for instance, pointed out that a false prediction refutes the corresponding theories: "any one contradictory instance overthrows a conjecture as to the Form" (NO II, xviii). However, both were aware, too, that theories are often not of a type which can be straightforwardly refuted, recognising that such theories may lead to empirical predictions only when taken together with other assumptions and that when one of these predictions fails, we cannot be sure which of the separate theories to blame. (Incidentally, the same problem applies, mutatis mutandis, to confirmations: when a group of theories makes a successful prediction, how much credit should each constituent be awarded? Neither Bacon nor Popper dealt with this equally pressing aspect of the problem.) Bacon and Popper each opposed the idea, which happened to be popular in both their philosophical milieux, that one is entitled to decide the question of which constituent to discard and what should replace it, in an arbitrary way or by fixing a 'convention', whose only limitation should be that the phenomena are saved. Bacon detected this attitude in the work of the alchemists and, as we shall see in a later chapter, of many astronomers too; their only motive, it seemed to him, was to preserve their principles, whatever the evidence. Popper also deplored this kind of approach to refutations, which he saw in the alchemical counterparts (as he would have judged them) of his day.

The successive theories that were advanced by alchemists after repeated failures to produce any gold, such as that there had been a "slip of a scruple in weight", were, no doubt, examples of the frivolous distinctions which Bacon mentioned in his general account of the method of anticipation. Popper called them "ad hoc". However, in Bacon's philosophy, they were not censured just for bringing a theory into line with what was previously an anomaly, for this would be a perfectly legitimate step in the interpretation of nature, always provided that the new theory led to new and verified predictions. A frivolous distinction is presumably one which fails to satisfy those conditions: it is an expedient whose *sole* function and virtue is to restore consistency with otherwise recalcitrant facts. It is thus identical to the notion of adhocness in Popper's philosophy, where a theory is said to be ad hoc either if it makes no novel empirical predictions as compared with its predecessor or, in case it does have some extra observational consequences, these have all been refuted. (1963, 244)

2(vii b) *The Plausibility of Bacon's Theory.*   These shared ideas of Bacon's and Popper's have a deal of plausibility, though I shall argue that this is removed by a more thorough examination. Consider first the plausible aspect: theories which might strike one as pretentious or unwarranted often turn out to have the characteristics which Bacon documented. Popper's nice example of Neptune's anger as a possible reason for why the sea is rough illustrates the point. This seems a pretty poor explanation. It also appears to possess one of the faults of anticipations, in that it makes no new predictions which could serve as further evidence to confirm its truth; it seems to have been "framed to the measure of those particulars only from which it is derived". This is a contrived example; a genuine one might be Medawar's impoverished explanation for why Eskimoes have a relatively high intelligence quotient. This result was unexpected by many, in view of the harsh poverty and poor education then afforded to the Eskimoes. Medawar proposed to explain the observation with the claim that their "upbringing in an igloo gives just the right degree of cosiness, security and mutual contact to conduce to a good performance in intelligence tests". As with the first example, this explanation seems to have been "cut to the precise measure of the familiar facts". There seems, therefore, to be some support for the Bacon-Popper diagnosis of the pathological element in these intuitively unsatisfactory explanations.

A prima facie case can also be made out for the second aspect of Bacon's criticism of anticipation, for it is a common technique, especially of the less successful kinds of investigation, for a theory to be defended to the bitter end, as it were, however adverse the evidence, by suitably varying auxiliary assumptions. A systematic policy of upholding a theory under these circumstances does indeed seem unscientific. Popper has argued, with what accuracy I cannot tell, that Marxism went this way, starting out as a conjecture full of untested predictions but ending up, after these had all failed, as untestable by any new predictions. Imre Lakatos and some of his students have made careful historical analyses of comparable instances in the history of science. (See, for example, the case-studies in Howson (1976).)

2(vii c) Some Difficulties in Bacon's Theory.   Bacon's criteria, then, appear to capture many of the judgments which later scientists and philosophers would make about the value of particular sciences. Unfortunately, however, they are open to powerful objections, which suggest that the characteristics picked out by them are not the true differentiae separating good from not-so-

good theories, but are merely accidental features often
accompanying each.

Bacon's criteria seem to be deficient in two separate respects.
First, they fix on a feature of theories and evidence, namely their
order of presentation, which appears to be strictly irrelevant; and,
second, they fail to discriminate against many theories that are
plainly unacceptable.

Take the first point. Bacon said that, to qualify as an
interpretation, a theory must lead to *new* predictions and that, if
it merely explains existing data, then it is an anticipation of
nature. Popper adopted a similar view: a theory is ad hoc and
hence (in Popper's view) inferior, if it takes account only of what is
known, without predicting novel phenomena. A number of
philosophers have recently followed Popper in adopting this rule:
Lakatos, for instance, declared that "for the sort of Popperian
empiricism I advocate, the only relevant evidence is the evidence
anticipated by a theory" (1970, 123).

However, telling objections can be made against this point of
view. First, suppose a theory is suggested in order to explain
certain data, but that it fails to lead to any new predictions. Bacon
would say that this is an anticipation of nature and Popper that it
is ad hoc. But imagine that another scientist is in possession of
only part of the data, and that he advances the very same theory
to explain the facts of which he is aware. The theory now does
lead to novel predictions; hence it interprets nature and is not ad
hoc. But this means that whether a theory is praised or
disparaged hangs not only on its relation to the evidence but also
on the historical accident of when the evidence was first cognized,
and this of course may vary from scientist to scientist. In assessing
a theory, we should have to ask who invented it and when, and in
cases of simultaneous discoveries, our conclusions could be very
different *for one and the same theory,* which I think would be
generally considered absurd. (This objection is discussed by
Hempel, 1966, 38, and by Frankel, 1979, 25.)

Another objection to the rule requiring novel predictions from
a theory is that it allows a theory to be both verified *and*
unsatisfactorily ad hoc. As a simple example, consider an urn that

powerful evidence. (This, incidentally, is roughly the way the problem would be tackled by the so-called Bayesian methodology, which exploits Bayes's theorem in the probability calculus to explicate scientific reasoning. This theorem relates what Bayesians term a theory's "prior" probability, $p(H)$, with its "posterior" probability, $p(H/e)$, i.e., the probability of H in the light of evidence, e; the value of a theory's posterior probability depends upon its prior probability, amongst other factors.)

2(viii) Summary

Bacon's scientific method has much in common with the more recent philosophy of Karl Popper. Both favour hypotheses that go beyond the original data; they share a preference that such hypotheses should deal with latent physical causes; and each insists that a new hypothesis should predict new phenomena. The two parties are also united in opposition to those merely saving devices employed when a theory is hit by adverse evidence. It appears too that both philosophers were led to these views as a reaction to instrumentalist or conventionalist doctrines, and in response to what they understood to be the obscurantist influence of such philosophies in the sterile and unproductive types of science current in their times.

The differences between the interpretation of nature and falsificationism are equally notable. Popper believed that the scientist should be as daring or "bold" as possible in advancing theories, while Bacon took the view that caution is preferable, and that one should approach theories of increasing generality by gradual stages.

Bacon's circumspect, step-by-step approach is the more reasonable. It is not good enough that a theory is merely consistent with the data, even if it happens to have anticipated some of them; it must also be a serious contender for the truth, that is to say, it should also be plausible or probable. And, as I stated earlier, the more speculative or general a statement is, the

less certain it will be. This, then, provides a rational foundation
for Bacon's gradualism, since the more speculative a claim, the
more evidence is needed to establish it.

That Bacon's method sets certainty as the goal, marks an even
more significant divergence from the Popperian approach. As
Popper himself said,

> the sole purpose of the elimination advocated by all these
> inductivists [Bacon, Whewell, and Mill] was to *establish as
> firmly as possible the surviving theory* which, they thought,
> must be the *true* one (or perhaps only a *highly probable* one
> . . .). (1959, 419)

By contrast, Popper believed that experimental tests, even so-
called crucial tests, "can at most refute or falsify a theory" (1963,
112), and he said that in general we should *"hold on to the most
improbable of the surviving theories"* (1959, 419). This, in Popper's
view, commits one to adopting theories with zero probability, that
is to say, theories which have the same chance of being true as do
contradictions and theories which have already been refuted!

It is not my intention to examine this eccentric conclusion any
more closely, save to repeat what I have already said, that the
Popperian method is far removed from what would be recognised
by most working scientists, for scientists are quite clearly
interested in *establishing* theories and in showing, largely by
experiment, that they are, in some sense, likely to be true.
Bacon's philosophy, on the other hand, takes this important fact
about scientific reasoning into account.

Many philosophers of science would, no doubt, still object to
Bacon's position as I have interpreted it, and argue that while a
theory may come to be believed with great conviction or to seem
more or less plausible, these various psychological states provide
no measure of a theory's *real* worth, for this is an *objective* matter
and, hence, independent of what any individual might think or
feel. Scientific method ought to deal with the real, 'objective
value' of a theory, as determined by some relation existing just
between it and the evidence. These are fine sentiments, and it

would, no doubt, be a noble achievement to have developed an appropriate concept and measure of a theory's objective value. But despite an immense effort which many distinguished philosophers (such as Carnap, Reichenbach, Jeffreys, Keynes, and even Popper) have applied to the problem, nothing approaching success can be reported. Instead, the programme has uncovered a hornet's nest of difficulties, which make confidence in its eventual success hard to sustain. It seems to me that the failure of the alternative programme rather diminishes the authority of the objection which might be levelled at Bacon, that he merely described the conditions under which scientists regard a theory as well or poorly supported. If Bacon's account is in some respects right, this represents a valuable advance in the understanding of scientific method.

Chapter Three
The Aims of Baconian Science

*For we cannot command nature
except by obeying her.* (NO I,
cxxix)

3(i) Speculative and Operative Science

In describing the various aspects and types of scientific
investigation, Bacon invented a number of divisions and
subdivisions which he thought would be helpful and instructive.
First of all, science was divided into 'speculative' and 'operative'
parts, corresponding roughly to the modern distinction between
pure science and technology; the former involved an "inquisition
into causes", the latter, the "production of effects". However, these
two are closely related in fairly obvious ways, for one reason
because effects, or particulars, precede the invention of axioms;
and then, secondly, because the discovery of new facts is largely
dependent on an understanding of causes. As he famously and
quotably said: "Knowledge . . . is power" (*Works* VII, 253); and

with similar meaning: "the roads to human power and to human knowledge lie close together, and are nearly the same" (NO II, iv).

3(ii) Physics

3(ii a) Efficient and Material Causes.   The speculative portion of science branches into two, *physics* and *metaphysics*, which are distinguished by the kinds of causes they handle. Adapting the classical four causes to his purpose, Bacon assigned so-called efficient and material causes to physics and final and formal causes to metaphysics.

Although he did not inquire into such philosophical questions as the nature of the connexion existing between a cause and its effects, his examples are very commonsensical and familiar. Thus, fire is the (efficient) cause of hardening in the case of clay (which in turn is the material cause of the change) and, similarly, fire causes the melting of wax.

But Bacon found a certain imperfection or inadequacy in causal explanations such as these, which appeal only to efficient and material causes. For, while it is true that, for instance, intermingling air and water always causes whiteness, this is "but very particular and restrained [as a method], being tied but to air and water" (VT, 236). Or, as he also put it, that "direction" for producing whiteness is "certain" but not "free". In modern jargon one would say that it provides sufficient, but not necessary, causal conditions for whiteness.

3(ii b) Latent Configurations and Processes.   Bacon reserved a further task for physics, namely, the investigation of the latent processes and latent configurations of ordinary bodies. The first covers the internal transformations of such processes as the generation of gold and other minerals, the development of herbs from seeds and the conception and growth of animals (NO II, v). Latent configurations of bodies concern such things as the concealed anatomical structures of men and animals, and the hidden constitutions of metals and plants. There is reason to think, said Bacon, that objects with a "specific character", such as iron and stone, have a "uniform structure" and it is this structure which he thought essential to disclose, particularly for science in its operative role. For "no one can endow a given body with a new nature, or successfully and aptly transmute it into a new body, unless he has attained a competent knowledge of the body so to be altered or transformed" (NO II, vii).

The investigations which Bacon envisaged were, he tells us, unlike most of the work conducted theretofore in that they concerned processes of development and structures which "for the most part . . . [escape] the sense" (NO II, vi). However, those methods of separation and analysis, such as distillation, which employ fire and heat to achieve their effects are inadequate to this task. The correct method would use "reasoning and true induction, with experiments to aid" (NO II, vii). Poetically expressed: "we must pass from Vulcan to Minerva, if we intend to bring to light the true textures and configurations of bodies; on which all the occult and, as they are called, specific properties and virtues in things depend" (NO II, vii). And prosaically, as Bacon stressed many times, it is crucial to look beneath the superficies of observable bodies for the causal determinants of their behaviour, not just with instruments and physical techniques but with the inductive method of speculation combined with experiment.

In brief, then, physics encompasses the study of efficient and material causes, and the underlying processes of development and the internal structures of ordinary bodies.

3(iii) Metaphysics and the Nature of Forms

3(iii a) Forms.   While Bacon briefed physics to deal with efficient and material causes, metaphysics was to take formal and final causes for its province. We shall postpone our discussion of final causes until the next chapter, save to remark that Bacon did not regard the reasons and purposes behind natural processes as being accessible by the usual experimental methods.

Bacon termed causes "formal" or "forms" when their presence not only produced the effect in question, as efficient and material causes do, but when, in addition, their absence prevented its appearance:

> the Form of a nature is such, that given the Form the nature infallibly follows. Therefore it is always present when the nature is present, and universally implies it, and is constantly inherent in it. Again, the Form is such, that if it be taken away the nature infallibly vanishes. Therefore it is always absent when the nature is absent, and implies its absence, and inheres in nothing else. (NO II, iv)

We could express this another way by saying, with Mary Horton (1973, 245), that the form of a nature includes both its necessary *and* sufficient causal conditions.

Bacon also talked of a form as being a "law" (e.g., NO II, ii) and as a "law of action or motion" (NO I, li), by which he presumably meant to convey that there is some kind of compulsion, analogous to the civil law, binding the form and its manifestation, that is to say, the two are related as cause and effect. As I have already remarked, he did not inquire into the nature of the bond involved in a causal or lawlike connexion, but this oversight (or, perhaps, preference for the simple life) does not vitiate the significance or meaningfulness of his concept of a form. For, even after a great deal of philosophical investigation, the nature of causality and the character of the relation existing between a cause and its effect are still not settled, and we are obliged to rest ordinary discussions of such matters upon the kind of intuitive understanding to which we normally pretend, the adequacy of which Bacon had no thought of challenging.

Forms, in Bacon's sense, are not often actually discovered in science, though a few examples exist. For instance, the presence of oxygen and hydrogen atoms, suitably linked and in the proportion 1:2, has been found to be both necessary and sufficient for the presence of water. Similarly, for light and electromagnetic radiation of a certain kind, and for the Morning and Evening Stars. In such cases, it is often considered convenient and appropriate to identify what had hitherto been regarded as separate entities, so that light and electromagnetic radiation, water and H_2O, and the Morning and Evening Stars would be regarded as the very same things.

   Bacon also thought it appropriate to identify a form with its corresponding nature: "the Form of a thing is the very thing itself, and the thing differs from the form no otherwise than as the apparent differs from the real, or the external from the internal, or the thing in reference to man from the thing in reference to the universe" (NO II, xiii). And when he advanced his suggestion that motion is the form of heat, he said: "When I say of Motion that it is as the genus of which heat is a species, I would be understood to mean, not that heat generates motion or that motion generates heat (though both are true in certain cases), but that Heat itself, its essence and quiddity, is Motion and nothing else" (NO II, xx).

3(iii b) *Examples of forms: Colour and Heat.*   Bacon presented two examples to illustrate the nature and structure of forms; they concern colour and heat, which we shall consider seriatim. Colour, Bacon suggested, is a matter of the proportions, presumably by size, existing between the smaller particles of a body. More specifically, particles which are "unequally equal, that is in a simple proportion", represent (as he said) whiteness, while "absolute equality produceth transparence", "inequality in compound or respective order or proportion produceth all other colours, and absolute or orderless inequality produceth blackness". He employed this account, we are told, principally as an illustration of forms rather than to exhibit a successful interpretation. Nevertheless, Bacon appears to have rested some confidence in it, expressing the opinion that it could explain numerous chromatic phenomena: "Out of this assertion [concerning the forms of colours] are satisfied a multitude of

effects and observations" (VT, 237). However, it is difficult to see
how the theory could be directed to explaining the absence of
blackness and whiteness from rainbows and the rarity of black
flowers, to take two of his examples.

But these problems apart, there is a further difficulty about
identifying those internal structures with the different colours.
For, although they may describe accurately circumstances which
produce colours in very many situations, they could not give all
the conditions which are both sufficient and necessary for colour
to be manifested. Bacon's theory could not, for instance, account
for the fact that "long beholding the snow to a weak eye giveth an
impression of azure rather than of whiteness" (VT, 238). This effect
clearly depends on the "intermedium" separating the object from
its beholder, as well as on the "act of sense". Although Bacon
bravely ventured the opinion that this is "a matter which is much
more easy to induce than that which we have passed through", his
valour did not extend to actually making the attempt, a reticence
which, in retrospect, is easily appreciated.

When Bacon came to expound the form of heat, the same
problem cropped up, though he dealt with it rather differently.
After a careful analysis of experiments and observations, which we
shall consider in more detail in due course, he concluded that
heat should be identified with a certain kind of motion in the
minute portions of matter. But, as he was aware, this alone could
not take in our perceptions or sensations of heat, for these depend
upon conditions other than those found in the external body. This
is shown by Bacon's example of "tepid water [which] feels hot if
the hand be cold, but cold if the hand be hot" (NO II, xiii), which
demonstrates that sensations of heat also depend on the way "the
senses are predisposed" (NO II, xx).

However, instead of planning to expand and further generalise
the conjectured form of heat, as he had done in the case of colour,
Bacon deftly distinguished two types of heat. The first is heat "in
relation to the universe", while the second "has relation to man
. . . and is correctly defined as merely the effect of heat on the
animal spirits" (NO II, xx). Bacon then identified the first of these

kinds of heat with a specific sort of motion among the minute particles of a body, describing that motion as the "essence and quiddity" of heat, and he dropped any further analysis of the second. (Bacon's theory of heat will be discussed in greater detail in Chapter Six.)

There is an element of what looks like chicanery in the distinction which Bacon drew between the two sorts of heat, because the original problem, which was to explain the nature of heat, as it is intuitively apprehended, is solved, or rather tackled, by describing the characteristics of some *other* state of affairs, which Bacon merely *called* "heat". From a scientific point of view, however, there is nothing wrong with the line Bacon took. For, although it may appear that he only advanced a definition, in reality he did much more. In particular, part of his claim was that the specific motion picked out and identified with heat is causally responsible for very many of the phenomena normally categorised as thermal. Thus he asserted that that motion explains the agitation of boiling liquids, the melting of metals, the expansion of heated air and much else. The scientific respectability of Bacon's approach is confirmed by the extraordinary fact that he arrived at an account of heat phenomena which in great measure anticipates today's view. Here, too, heat is identified, in a sort of 'creative definition', with a type of motion in a body's constituent parts, and this motion is employed as an essential explanatory principle for most thermal effects. Like Bacon, modern science has not found it rewarding to conflate all thermal phenomena under a single explanatory head; like him, it leaves sensations of heat to be accounted for by different means.

But while Bacon scored a small scientific success, seen from his own philosophical standpoint, his efforts must be judged a mitigated failure; for he did not arrive at the forms of either colour or heat, at least not if forms are understood in the Baconian manner as the necessary and sufficient conditions for the manifestation of these phenomena. As we saw, he conceded that his speculation on the form of colour fell short of the ideal. In the case of heat, Bacon made a show of having gained his end, by the

ingenious device of the two kinds of heat. But the form he
proposed, if taken to refer to the first kind of heat, is merely a
definition, which would have required no observations to
formulate and establish: if it refers to the second—and Bacon
denied that it could—it is plainly inadequate.

3(iv) Forms as Ideals

The difficulty which Bacon encountered in his search for a
genuine form-like cause is testimony that Baconian forms are
highly ambitious goals for science, and it shows that, in practice,
we must usually be satisfied if we discover just some of the
sufficient and some of the necessary conditions for the effects
under investigation. But this is not to say that Bacon was
misguided: quite the contrary. He envisaged metaphysics and the
forms it was supposed to reveal as an ideal, albeit an achievable
one, but one, too, which must be approached gradually, as the
class of conditions sufficient for the effect to be manifested is
widened. The knowledge of such conditions has a practical
advantage, for it "frees the direction", that is, it opens up new
means for bringing about a desired effect. But there was also a
theoretical benefit from such knowledge, in that it permitted a
wider range of manifestations of a phenomenon, such as colour or
heat, to be encompassed and explained by a single explanatory
principle, an end which Bacon thought desirable:

> it is the duty and virtue of all knowledge to abridge the
> circuits and long ways of experience (as much as truth will
> permit), and to remedy the ancient complaint that "life is
> short and art is long." And this is best performed by
> collecting and uniting the axioms of sciences into more
> general ones, and such as may comprehend all individual
> cases. (DA 3iv, 361)

> So then always that knowledge is worthiest which least
> burdens the intellect with multiplicity. (DA 3iv, 362)

Forms thus stand near the apex of a pyramid of more and more general causes and axioms, and emerge gradually, at the end of what Bacon called "progressive stages of certainty" (NO, preface). His sketched induction of the nature of whiteness illustrates these stages. The induction is initiated with the observation that air and water, intermingled, produce whiteness, and continues with the discovery that air mingled with *any* transparent body is white. Bacon then "removes the restraint" that an uncoloured body must be used, as finely powdered amber and beer brought to a froth are also white. The class of bodies that can serve to produce whiteness is now widened still further, by considering materials other than air, and we finally arrive, by what Bacon seems to concede is too precipitate a leap, at the tentative formulation of the form of whiteness which we have described. (VT, 236–7)

The analogy whereby knowledge of increasing generality is arranged in a pyramidal hierarchy is, as a matter of fact, Bacon's own. He likened the base of the pyramid to "history and experience" (DA 3iv, 362), that is to say, to the observable phenomena, which are "infinite in number" (DA 2xiii, 321). The next stage above that represents physics; then comes metaphysics; and finally, at the apex of the pyramid, what Bacon called "summary philosophy". Summary philosophy, which Bacon also denominated *philosophia prima*, was envisaged as bestriding all the other sciences by virtue of its great generality: it is a "universal science . . . [and] the mother of the rest". (DA 3i, 337) He gave a number of examples of axioms which qualify as primitive in this sense. One is that "if equals be added to unequals the wholes will be unequal", a principle which holds not only in regard to numbers in mathematics but also applies to justice, in ethics (DA 3i, 337).

Rather confusingly, Bacon sometimes talked of the "cone and vertical point of the pyramid" being occupied by "the summary law of nature", to which, he said, "it may fairly be doubted whether man's inquiry can attain". The summary law of nature does not seem to be the same as summary philosophy, for Bacon conceived it as the ultimate law of nature. He set out this idea

most clearly in the *De Sapientia Veterum*, when expounding the
fable of Cupid, whose hidden meaning concerned the atom.
Bacon took Cupid, or Love, "to be the appetite or instinct of
primal matter; or to speak more plainly, *the natural motion of the
atom;* which is indeed the original and unique force that
constitutes and fashions all things out of matter." Then he
described the summary law of nature as being "that impulse of
desire impressed by God upon the primary particles of matter
which makes them come together, and which by repetition and
multiplication produces all the variety of nature". Unlike other
laws, however, "the single and summary law" cannot be further
explained, for the primitive appetite of atoms "is entirely without
parent; that is, without cause . . . And even if it were possible to
know the method and process of it, yet to know it by way of cause
is not possible; it being, next to God, the cause of causes—itself
without cause" (*Works* VI, 729–30). Bacon offered no argument for
the existence of a single, ultimate law governing the atoms.

I see no evidence for L. J. Cohen's claim (1980, 220) that the
forms themselves are arranged in a pyramidal hierarchy. His view
is derived from the following statement of Bacon's: "For a true and
perfect axiom of knowledge then the direction and precept will
be, *that another nature be discovered which is convertible with
the given nature, and yet is a limitation of a more intelligible
nature, as of a true and real genus*" (NO II, iv). Cohen says that,
in view of Bacon's examples, "we have to suppose that such a more
fundamental nature may itself have a form that investigators seek
to discover" (1980, 220).

Thus Cohen argues that, while Bacon conjectures the form of
heat to be a certain restricted motion, he also "treats motion itself
as a nature that may be investigated in the same way as heat is
investigated" (1980, 220). But the investigation to which Cohen
directs us in order to back this up is rather different from the one
concerned with the form of heat. Bacon was explaining the
operation of a particular sort of experimental observation—which
he called an "Instance of Alliance or Union"—whose task was to

demonstrate that two effects, initially supposed to be heterogeneous, are in fact "only a modification of a common nature" (NO II, xxxv). He exemplified this with solar heat and the ordinary heat of a fire, both of which ripen grapes and are, therefore, not essentially heterogeneous. The investigation regarding motion was, similarly, designed to inquire into the "received division" that heavenly bodies necessarily move with the perpetual motion of rotation, that the earth is essentially at rest, and that other bodies are either by their nature carried upward if they are light, or turn towards the earth if heavy. All this "pretty talk" is exploded by "one of the lower comets, which though far below the heaven, nevertheless revolve", and by the east-west rotation of the air within the tropics. These desultory observations were not, then, intended to reveal the form of motion as the specific expression of some other, more fundamental, quality or nature, but were merely introduced in order to test particular theories about the natural motions of certain bodies. They therefore do not support Cohen's contention of a hierarchy of forms.

To summarise this section, Bacon hoped science would advance, in stages, to greater and greater universality, eventually attaining the forms of simple properties, which represent a certain very high degree of generality. The fact that this stage of science may not be reachable in practice does not detract from Bacon's insight that science would progress by seeking ever more general axioms or theories, in order to explain as much as possible by the fewest principles.

3(v) Forms of the First and Second Class

Bacon made a distinction between different kinds of form, namely elementary and compound forms, or forms of simple properties and of substances, calling the former "forms of the first class". He thought that, in view of the part-whole relation existing between them, it would be easier and of more practical value to begin by investigating the elementary forms:

> For as it would be neither easy nor of any use to inquire the form of the sound which makes any word . . . whereas to inquire the form of the sound which makes any simple letter . . . is comprehensible, nay easy; and yet these forms of letters once known will lead us directly to the forms of words; so in a like manner to inquire the form of a lion, of an oak, of gold, nay even of water or air, is a vain pursuit; but to inquire the form of dense, rare, hot, cold, heavy, light, tangible, pneumatic, volatile, fixed, and the like, as well as configurations as motions, which in treating of Physic I have in great part enumerated (I call them *Forms of the First Class*), and which (like the letters of the alphabet) are not many and yet make up and sustain the essences and forms of all substances;—this, I say, it is which I am attempting, and which constitutes and defines that part [concerning forms] of Metaphysic of which we are now inquiring. (DA 3iv, 360–1)

It is hard to disagree with Bacon that discovering the necessary and sufficient conditions for the existence and nature of a lion, or of gold, or of an oak, would be immeasurably more difficult a task than doing the same for some of the properties that these compound bodies possess. Subsequent developments in science seem to bear this out.

But the claim that there are just a *few* such basic properties, which combine in a variety of ways to produce the huge multiplicity of concrete objects, is much less plausible. For objects clearly possess very many, perhaps infinitely many, properties. Bacon's claim could be granted if most of these were established as somehow derivative from a small set of elementary properties, but there is no reason to expect that this could be achieved and, a fortiori, no grounds for selecting certain properties in advance as elementary.

Bacon's unhappy claim that compound bodies are analysable into a small number of properties has been used, unjustly I believe, as a main support in what I earlier called the standard interpretation. It will be remembered that the inductive process, in that interpretation, was initiated by an exhaustive analysis of a compound body, such as gold, into its constituent simple natures (yellowness, ductility, and so on). But it should be noted that Bacon's claim about the constitution of compound bodies was not advanced in the context of induction to causes. It was used either to argue, as in the last quotation (and also at NO II, viii), that it would be much easier to study simple properties than concrete bodies, or else to establish that a knowledge of those properties would be of great assistance in the operative, or applied, part of science.

Thus the analysis of gold into some of its natures, which I quoted in Chapter One as part of the evidence supporting the standard interpretation, was brought into the discussion by Bacon to explain how the operative part of science works. It will be recalled that the task of this part was "to generate and superinduce a new nature or new natures" on a given body; it is "the work and aim of Human Power" and is sharply distinguished from the discovery of forms, which by contrast is "the work and aim of Human Knowledge" (NO II, i). Bacon argued that, once the forms of the various simple natures have been discovered, a knowledge of the constitution of compound bodies, such as gold, might enable one to create such a body out of another: "For he who knows the forms of yellow, weight, ductility, fixity, fluidity, solution, and so on, and the methods for superinducing them, and their gradations and modes, will make it his care to have them joined together in some body, whence may follow the transformation of that body into gold" (NO II, v).

Thus Bacon's explicit statements in favour of a sort of alphabet of nature, with simple properties corresponding to the letters, were not expressed with induction in mind but were intended to underpin the two claims I have mentioned: (a) that it is easier to investigate simple natures than compound bodies, and (b) that a knowledge of simple natures will lead to practical methods for transmuting substances. However, while there is no direct evidence that the alphabet of nature thesis formed the basis of

Bacon's inductive method, his model investigation into the nature of heat is often cited as indirect evidence. That investigation is discussed in detail in Chapter Six, where I think it will become apparent that it does not in fact presuppose an alphabet of nature.

3(vi) Atomism

3(vi a) Introduction.   As we saw earlier, a Baconian interpretation should, ideally, penetrate beneath the surface and reach to the internal causes of things, and we should thus expect forms to be connected with these latent causes. Indeed, the two examples of forms worked out by Bacon are both expressed in terms of the smaller and evidently invisible particles of matter. However, these particles are not necessarily ultimate particles, for Bacon averred that the motion constituting the form of heat resided not in the finest particles, but in those of "a degree larger". It is not clear whether these somewhat larger particles were a composite of the smaller ones, or whether they were different in type, though Bacon's ideas on atomism, which we are about to deal with, strongly suggest the former.

Bacon was one of the first English philosophers to give serious attention to the ancient theory of atoms. I shall argue that he was very sympathetic to a kind of atomism, and that this underpinned his view of forms as having a corpuscular basis. However, it has often been claimed that, while Bacon originally took a favourable view of atomism, he positively rejected it in his maturer philosophy. I wish to show that Bacon did not, in fact, change his mind about the existence of atoms, though he did give up the idea that the atoms were separated by empty space.

3(vi b) Two Kinds of Atomism.   In Bacon's earliest detailed discussion of Democritus's atomism he said that it is "either true or useful for demonstration. For it is not easy either to grasp in thought or to express in words the genuine subtlety of nature,

such as it is found in things, without supposing an atom".
(Thoughts on the Nature of Things, Works V, 419). However,
Bacon discerned two kinds of atomism in the writings of the
ancients and he wished to be associated with only one of them.
The first takes an atom to be "the last term or smallest portion of
the division or fraction of bodies", while the second defines it as
"a body without vacuity", that is to say, a perfectly solid body
containing no empty spaces. *(Works* V, 419) Bacon evidently
approved of the first kind of atomism, for he said that it "may be
safely and certainly laid down" (a) "that there is in things a much
more subtle distribution and comminution than falls under view"
and (b) "that this is not however infinite nor perpetually divisible."
(my italics)

The second sort of atomism, which "presupposes a vacuum
[quod vacuum praesupponit], and defines an atom as that which
is without a vacuum" was, however, not accepted by Bacon, for he
was not prepared unquestioningly to concede the existence of a
vacuum. He followed Hero in distinguishing a "vacuum
interspersed" from a "large or collected vacuum". The first of
these, which occupies the spaces between the particles of matter,
seemed to him necessary to explain the capacity of bodies to be
compressed and to expand. The second, on the other hand, was
denied with "a good and earnest diligence on the part of Hero",
in view of the evident resistance that nature offers when an
extended vacuum might be formed. Bacon believed, however, that
Hero went a bit too far and showed himself inferior to Democritus
when he "simply denied" the existence of a collected vacuum, for
"there is no reason why in the regions of the air, where there are
doubtless greater expansions of bodies, there may not be also a
collected vacuum." *(Works* V, 420–1)

However, Bacon's atomism departed from Democritean
atomism in some respects. First of all, Bacon did not insist that all
changes occur through atomic collision. He said that "whoever
maintains the theory of the atom and the vacuum . . . necessarily
implies the action of the virtue of the atom at a distance: for
without this no motion could be originated, by reason of the

vacuum interposed" (*De Sapientia Veterum,* 731). Bacon was
evidently assuming here that the atoms must at all times be
separated by a vacuum, but he gave no explanation for this
supposed necessity. The claim about atoms acting at a distance
was not, however, repeated in Bacon's second attempt to interpret
the fable of Cupid, in his *Principles and Origins.* The reason for
this may be that, as we shall see, he seems eventually to have
abandoned the vacuum hypothesis.

The second divergence from Democritus concerns the nature
of the atoms. Democritus maintained that the ultimate particles
differed both in their sizes and shapes, while Bacon was more
inclined to think that they were "altogether equal and similar", a
view he tentatively traced to Pythagoras. Bacon observed that the
reason why Democritus had postulated primitive differences in
atoms was not decisive, being based on a denial that "all things
may be made out of all things". But, as Bacon pointed out, even if
the ultimate particles were all the same, they might join up to
form different substances in such a way that it could still prove
impossible in practice to transmute one substance into another:

> For there is no doubt but that the seeds of things, though
> equal, as soon as they have thrown themselves into certain
> groups and knots, completely assume the nature of dissimilar
> bodies, till those groups or knots are dissolved; so that the
> nature and affections of compound bodies may be as great a
> hindrance and obstacle to immediate transmutation as those
> of simple. (*Works* V, 422)

Bacon then described a number of observations which he thought
would prepare "a way to the overthrow of the theory of
Democritus on the diversity of seeds or atoms". (*Works* V, 423)

Although Bacon gave the impression that he sided with a form
of atomism, and even regarded the existence of minute, ultimate,
particles as "safely and securely laid down", one leading scholar,
Graham Rees, has maintained that the favour Bacon showed
towards atomism "never rose above benevolent neutrality" (1980,
555). In Rees's view, Bacon could not have committed himself to
atomism for, he claims, that doctrine was incompatible with a

"pneumatic theory of matter", which he regards as central to Bacon's cosmology.

According to this theory, many natural processes, such as the rusting of iron and the conversion of wine into vinegar, are controlled by extremely tenuous, weightless, and subtle spirits. These spirits, which Bacon conceived as being "akin to air", combined with tangible bodies, but, like air, they could also exist in a free state. (He employed these ideas in his histories of life and death and of dense and rare, and in a number of other places. The best account of them was presented in 1938 by Joshua Gregory.) Rees takes the view that, for Bacon, spirits, unlike atoms, were non-material substances, and hence inexplicable in atomic terms.

The weightlessness that Bacon attributed to the spirits might, indeed, suggest immateriality. On the other hand, Bacon also regarded some definitely material bodies as weightless, for instance, a speck of dust, which "appeareth, but weigheth not". And he conjectured that "a dense and compact mass" would lose its weight if removed to a sufficient distance from the earth, and that it would then "hang like the earth itself, and not fall unless thrust down." (NO II, xxxv) More importantly, the atoms themselves were imponderable, in Bacon's scheme, even though, in combination, they were capable of producing a heavy body. This may sound a little strange, but it is evidently in line with the views of Democritus, who also appears to have regarded weight as a derivative property of atoms. (See Bailey, 1928, 128–32.) Bacon, clearly, considered weight to be a property analogous to heat, which was created when numbers of particles, which were themselves neither hot nor cold, were suitably agitated.

> Atoms . . . are neither like sparks of fire, nor drops of water, nor bubbles of air, nor grains of dust, nor particles of spirit or ether. Neither is their power and form heavy or light, hot or cold, dense or rare, hard or soft, such as those qualities appear in greater bodies; since these and others of the kind are results of composition and combination. (*On Principles and Origins*, Works V, 464)

Hence, the imponderability of spirits renders them no less material than the atoms themselves, and certainly does not mean that they may not be composed of material atoms.

Rees also argues that Bacon held light and sound to be immaterial, spiritual, substances, his main evidence being a remark in the *Sylva Sylvarum* (p. 317), where Bacon said of light and sound that they "do not appear to emit any corporal substance into their mediums . . . neither again to raise or stir any evident local motion in their mediums as they pass; but only to carry certain spiritual species." But this remark certainly does not imply that the spiritual species were immaterial; it is perfectly consistent with light's being a very fine, material substance, which passes through bodies without appearing to impart any of its matter and without producing any evident local motion. In fact, however, Bacon seems to have opposed a material theory of light and sound; but this by no means divorced him from an atomic explanation, for it is compatible with light's being a form of vibrational energy, transmitted via atoms. Indeed, something of this sort may have been in Bacon's mind, for he concluded that light and sound were both "energies merely". (*Sylva*, 652)

In conclusion, Rees's objections notwithstanding, Bacon seems to have been very well disposed towards an atomic theory in which matter is composed of minute, identical, indivisible particles, acting on each other at a distance, and separated by empty space.

3(vi c) Did Bacon Change his Mind on Atomism?   Most of the discussion from which the above conclusion was drawn appears in Bacon's *Thoughts on the Nature of Things,* which Spedding tentatively placed at a date before 1605. It is often maintained that Bacon's initial sympathy towards atomism altered completely, in his later philosophy, into an attitude of rather definite opposition. (See, for example, Hesse, 1964, 149, 151; and Kargon, 1966). The evidence for Bacon's supposed volte face and eventual antipathy to atomism comes from the *Novum Organum,* in particular from the following:

Nor again is it a less evil, that in their philosophies and
contemplations their labour is spent in investigating and
handling the first principles of things and the highest
generalities of nature; whereas utility and the means of
working result entirely from things intermediate. Hence it is
that men cease not from abstracting nature till they come to
potential and unformed *(informem)* matter, nor on the other
hand from dissecting nature till they reach the atom; things
which, even if true, can do but little for the welfare of
mankind. (NO I, lxvi)

Nor shall we thus [by true induction] be led to the doctrine
of atoms, which implies the hypothesis of a vacuum *[qui
praesupponit Vacuum]* and that of the unchangeableness of
matter (both false assumptions); we shall be led only to real
particles, such as really exist. (NO II, viii)

The first of these quotations is not a denial of atomism at all but
merely a warning that, as far as practical effects are concerned,
little can be expected from speculation upon them, though it
seems likely that it was just *premature* speculation that Bacon had
in mind here, in which case his remarks would be more easily
explicable.

Consider the second quotation. It is odd for Bacon to allege
that atomism implies "the unchangeableness of matter", since he
had earlier explained that this is a consequence only of
Democritean atomism, in which the ultimate particles differed in
size and shape. The atomic hypothesis he had favoured postulated
identical atoms, which, by being thrown into "certain groups and
knots, completely assume the nature of dissimilar bodies".
Substances are then interconvertible, at least in principle, since
they are just composed of the same particles in different
arrangements.

Bacon also described the atomism that he was rejecting as one
which "implies the hypothesis of a vacuum *[qui praesupponit
Vacuum]*". It will be remembered that Bacon had earlier
considered two types of atomism, one of which presupposed a
vacuum *("quod vacuum praesupponit")*, and which he had

criticized for unquestioningly assuming that a vacuum exists.

These two points suggest that the atomism which Bacon repudiated in the *Novum Organum* was just the same atomism he had earlier rejected in the *Thoughts on the Nature of Things*. It also suggests that he was not repenting of his earlier sympathy towards that form of the doctrine which permitted the transmutation of any one substance into any other and whose definition does not prejudge the question of the vacuum. This would explain his continued belief in the existence of what he called "real particles".

It is evident, too, that Bacon retained a conviction that observable phenomena result from the actions of minute and invisible particles and that scientific explanations and forms should take account of them. For, in the *Sylva Sylvarum*, one of his last works, he said this clearly:

> The knowledge of man (hitherto) hath been determined by the view or sight; so that whatsoever is invisible, either in respect of the fineness of the body itself, or the smallness of the parts, or of the subtilty of the motion, is little inquired. And yet these be the things that govern nature principally; and without which you cannot make any true analysis and indication of the proceedings of nature. (p. 380)

> And for the more subtile differences of the minute parts, and the posture of them in the body, (which also hath great effects,) they are not at all touched: as for the motions of the minute parts of bodies, which do so great effects, they have not been observed at all; because they are invisible, and incur not to the eye; but yet they are to be deprehended by experience: as Democritus said well, when they charged him to hold that the world was made of such little motes as we were seen in the sun: *Atomus*, saith he, *necessitate rationis et experientiae esse convincitur; atomum nemo unquam vidit.* ['We are convinced of the existence of the atom by the necessity of reason and experience; for no one has ever seen an atom'.] (p. 381)

3(vii) Bacon's Views on the Vacuum

The discussion of atomism in the *Novum Organum,* however, departs from Bacon's earlier statements in regard to the vacuum, in that he now abandons his previously quite favourable attitude towards the two sorts of vacuum, calling the hypothesis of a vacuum a "false assumption". Rees has argued that this means Bacon "cannot be counted as an atomic philosopher" because "if there were no vacuum atoms would occupy all space and would no longer be distinguishable". (1980, 556) On the other hand, Bacon himself never addressed this apparent consequence of his position, and seems to have been quite unaware of it. He could have dealt with the difficulty by postulating non-homogeneous atoms, or by conceding atoms of different kinds, but it is hard to determine whether he would have been prepared to take either of these steps.

Bacon's peremptory dismissal of the vacuum hypothesis in the passage quoted above from the *Novum Organum* is particularly surprising since, in the very same work, he was "not prepared to say for certain whether or no there be a vacuum, either collected in one place or interspersed in the pores of bodies". (NO II, xlviii) It is difficult to know how to resolve this contradiction.

Bacon did, however, explain why he withdrew his positive support for an interspersed vacuum. First of all, he argued, on the basis of specific gravities which he had himself determined, that if there were an interspersed vacuum, then air must have "two thousand times as much of vacuity as there is in gold". But if this were so, he argued, then one could not account for "the potency of the virtues of pneumatical bodies (which otherwise would be floating in empty space like fine dust)". Bacon also mentioned "many other proofs" that air could not contain so much vacuum, though he did not elaborate on these. Secondly, he altered his former stand and now denied, what he had earlier affirmed, that an interspersed vacuum was needed to explain expansion and contraction. An alternative explanation existed, Bacon claimed, because "matter is clearly capable of folding and unfolding itself in space, within certain limits, without the interposition of a vacuum" (NO II, xlviii).

Unfortunately, Bacon did not clarify this obscure claim. However, we have some guide to his meaning from his early discussion of expansion and contraction, in the *Thoughts on the Nature of Things* (pp. 420–1). He stated there that only three explanations could account for the phenomena. The first was that contraction happens "by the exclusion of vacuum", which, as I said, Bacon afterwards rejected in the light of his specific gravity measurements; the second proposed that there is no vacuum, but that substances expand by absorbing external material and contract by expelling material enclosed within them; and according to the third theory, expansion and contraction worked "by some natural (whatever that may be) condensation and rarefaction of bodies", whereby "the same bodies, not otherwise changed, do yet admit of more or less in density or rarity".

Bacon traced this last theory to Aristotle and he rejected it as barely worth considering: "it need not be much laboured. For it seems to be something positive, depending on a supposition incapable of further explanation, as Aristotle's assertions generally do". (*Works* V, 421). Mary Hesse has suggested that this was the view he was embracing when he argued that contraction and expansion were brought about by matter "folding and unfolding itself in space". But since Bacon's earlier dismissal of the idea was so uncompromising, it is rather more likely, I shall suggest, that the second theory was the one he finally adopted.

Bacon's original criticism of the second theory is difficult to understand. Rather surprisingly, he dealt only with the specific version of the theory according to which a body expels a material "finer" than itself when it contracts:

> Now with regard to the forcing out of a finer body, that process seems to have no end. It is true indeed that sponges and the like porous bodies are contracted when the air is squeezed out; but it is shown by many experiments that the air itself admits of a considerable contraction. Are we then to

suppose that the finer part of the air is squeezed out, and out of that part another, and so on for ever? Such an opinion is strongly opposed by the fact that the finer bodies are, the greater is the contraction they admit of; whereas it should be the contrary, if contraction proceeded from the forcing out of the finer part. (*Works* V, 421–2)

However this rather obscure argument is assessed, it does not discredit the idea that contraction happens "by the forcing out of some other body previously intermixed", which Bacon had represented as one of only three ways in which contraction could be explained, unless that process necessarily involved the expulsion of a "finer" material. But Bacon never specified precisely what he meant by "fineness" in this context and he gave no evidence for the counterintuitive claim that a finer, and more contractible, body is invariably forced out in contraction.

I suggest, though this must be a tentative suggestion, that Bacon came to realize his arguments had not discredited the possibility that contraction results from "the forcing out of some other body previously intermixed" and that this was the account he favoured in the *Novum Organum,* when he described the processes of contraction and absorption in terms of "matter folding and unfolding itself in space . . . without the interposition of a vacuum".

3(viii) Conclusion

Bacon envisaged science as starting out from particular instances of a property, such as whiteness or heat, then proceeding to theories concerning the efficient and material conditions which cause that property to be manifested, and finally arriving at the formal cause of the property. It appears that the second stage, which Bacon included in physics, was intended to uncover more and more general conditions under which the properties in question are produced, after which the transition would finally be made to metaphysics, with the discovery of both the necessary and the sufficient conditions, that is to say, the forms.

Bacon clearly believed that the phenomena of nature were produced by the actions of minute, invisible, material particles, though the details of his atomic theory were hazy and underwent some changes, particularly in regard to whether the particles were separated by a vacuum or not. The forms, through which phenomena are explained and understood, must deal with the actions of the small (though not necessarily the smallest) particles of matter, as Bacon's own examples did.

Chapter Four
The Idols

For what a man had rather were true he more readily believes. (NO I, xlix)

4(i) Introduction

Bacon's doctrine of the idols is one of the most famous parts of his philosophy. The idols were "fallacies of the mind of man" or "false appearances", mental attitudes of a certain kind, which needed to be "cleared away" and "purged", before the business of science could be started properly. Indeed, the sterility of so much of the scientific work that Bacon reviewed was caused, so he thought, by the intrusion of idols. It is easy to gain the impression from his writings that the idols were theories, or perhaps propensities to form theories, and that by their expulsion the mind would become an empty box, as it were, into which infallible factual reports could pour (again as it were). This is how a number of philosophers have understood Bacon. For instance, Popper:

> Bacon's view was that, to prepare the mind for the intuition of
> the true *essence* or *nature* of a thing, it has to be
> meticulously cleansed of all anticipations, prejudices, and
> idols. For the source of all error is the impurity of our own
> minds: Nature itself does not lie. The main function of
> eliminative induction is (as with Aristotle) to assist the
> purification of the mind . . . Purging the mind of prejudices
> is conceived as a kind of ritual prescribed for the scientist,
> analogous to the mystic's purification of his soul to prepare it
> for the vision of God. (1959, 279)

Popper also spoke of authors who, "Like Bacon, . . . pin their hopes on the empty mind" (1973, 394). Mary Hesse has a similar interpretation: "All this [the idols], says Bacon, must be purged and swept away. The mind is to be made into, what Locke was later to say it is naturally, a *'tabula abrasa'*" (1964, 144) Similarly, it has been said that, for Bacon, "the mind must be freed from all assumptions" (Alexander, 1907, 151). And Morris Cohen regarded Bacon's ideal scientist as one who "begins without any regard for previous thought. Resolved not to anticipate nature, he lets the facts record their own tale" (1949, 104).

Although I shall argue that these views misrepresent Bacon, it must be admitted that he did sometimes seem to say of the mind that it is best suited for science when freed from every opinion, and that only the idols stand in the way of this desirable state. For example, apparently in reference to the idols, he remarked:

> Such then are the provisions I make for finding the genuine
> light of nature and kindling and bringing it to bear. And they
> would be sufficient of themselves, if the human intellect were
> even, and like a fair sheet of paper with no writing on it. But
> since the minds of men are strangely possessed and beset, so
> that there is no true and even surface left to reflect the
> genuine rays of things, it is necessary to seek a remedy for
> this also. (*Plan*, 26–7)

And, concluding his description of the various idols in the *Novum Organum*, he said that they must all be "renounced and put away with a fixed and solemn determination, and the understanding thoroughly freed and cleansed; the entrance into the kingdom of man, founded on the sciences, being not much other than the entrance into the kingdom of heaven, whereunto none may enter except as a little child" (NO I, lxviii).

Peripheral remarks such as these, in which Bacon was either announcing or summarising his opinions, might well incline one to the *tabula rasa* interpretation. However, there are indications that the fair-sheet-of-paper analogy needs to be approached warily, for Bacon's earliest exposition of the idols contained an express denial that the mind could be brought to that immaculate condition:

> On waxen tablets you cannot write anything new until you
> rub out the old. With the mind it is not so; there you cannot
> rub out the old till you have written in the new. (MBT, 72)

But the clearest information about the idols comes from Bacon's detailed exposition of them. I shall argue that this shows his primary concern to have been with various patterns and causes of dogmatic and erroneous reasoning, the idols being particular species of these. We shall see that neither his descriptions of the idols nor his provisions for their removal make it necessary or desirable for scientists to strive for an empty mind, and that the types of attitude which he classed as unscientific are all of a piece with the hypothetico-inductive philosophy of science already described. The similarity of Bacon's and Popper's conceptions of bad science, to which I have already alluded, emerges particularly clearly in the discussion of the idols, a point I shall illustrate, in passing, by occasionally juxtaposing their remarks.

4(ii) The Idols of the Tribe and of the Cave

Bacon divided the idols into four types. The first, the idols of the *Tribe*, were ones to which we are all subject: they "have their foundation in human nature itself" (NO I, xli). The first of these was explained clearly by Bacon:

BACON

The human understanding is of its own nature prone to suppose the existence of more order and regularity in the world than it finds. And though there be many things in nature which are singular and unmatched, yet it devises for them parallels and conjugates and relatives which do not exist. (NO I, xlv)

POPPER

Our propensity to look out for regularities, and to impose laws upon nature, leads to the psychological phenomenon of *dogmatic thinking* or, more generally, dogmatic behaviour: we expect regularities everywhere and attempt to find them even where there are none; . . . (1963, 49)

Bacon also noticed that a predilection for order could lead to dogmatism, and he made this one of the central points in his case against the idols. He argued that once a theory ascribing a simple pattern to the phenomena has been advanced, people are inclined to render it immune from all criticism and thereby to misjudge the strength of its empirical support. This kind of dogmatism has two aspects. First of all, there is the tendency to pay selective attention to a theory's successes and altogether to ignore its failures: "a few times hitting or presence produces a much stronger impression on the mind than many times failing or absence" (DA 5iii, 432). Secondly, a theory may be permanently sheltered from criticism by the devising of suitable "distinctions", to deflect any adverse evidence:

BACON

The human understanding when it has once adopted an opinion (either as being the received opinion or as being agreeable to itself) draws all things else to support and agree with it. And though there be a greater number and weight of instances to be found on the other side, yet these it either neglects and despises, or else by some distinction sets aside

POPPER

events which do not yield to these attempts [to find regularities] we are inclined to treat as a kind of "background noise"; and we stick to our expectations even when they are inadequate and we ought to accept defeat. (1963, 49) Some genuinely testable theories, when found to be false *(sic)*, are still upheld by their admirers—for example by and rejects; in order that by this great and pernicious predetermination the authority of its former conclusions may remain inviolate. (NO I, xlvi)

introducing *ad hoc* some auxiliary assumption, or by re-interpreting the theory *ad hoc* in such a way that it escapes refutation. (1963, 37)

The tendency to overlook unfavourable evidence, or to reinterpret it so that a pet theory is forever immunised against criticism, is a characteristic weakness of many of the disciplines which Bacon regarded as inadequate and which, he believed, posed a serious danger to science:

BACON

And such is the way of all superstition, whether in astrology, dreams, omens, divine judgments, or the like; wherein men, having a delight in such vanities, mark the events where they are fulfilled, but where they fail, though this happen much oftener, neglect and pass them by. But with far more subtlety does this mischief insinuate itself into philosophy and the sciences; in which the first conclusion colours and brings into conformity with itself all that come after, though far sounder and better. (NO I, xlvi)

POPPER

For the dogmatic attitude is clearly related to the tendency to *verify* our laws and schemata by seeking to apply them and to confirm them, even to the point of neglecting refutations . . . (1963, 50)

The Marxist theory of history, in spite of the serious efforts of some of its founders and followers, ultimately adopted this soothsaying practice [of astrology "to predict things so vaguely that the predictions can hardly fail"]. In some of its earlier formulations . . . their predictions were testable, and in fact falsified. Yet instead of accepting the refutations the followers of Marx re-interpreted both the theory and the evidence in order to make them agree. (1963, 37)

Bacon restated the danger when dealing with the second set of idols—those of the *Cave*—which "take their rise in the peculiar constitution, mental or bodily, of each individual; and also in education, habit and accident." (NO I, liii) The chief hazard here is that:

BACON	POPPER
Men become attached to certain particular sciences and speculations, either because they fancy themselves the authors and inventors thereof, or because they have bestowed the greatest pains upon them and become most habituated to them. But men of this kind, if they betake themselves to philosophy and contemplations of a general character, distort and colour them in obedience to their former fancies . . . (NO I, liv)	I may perhaps mention here a point of agreement with psycho-analysis. Psycho-analysts assert that neurotics and others interpret the world in accordance with a personal set pattern which is not easily given up, and which can often be traced back to early childhood. A pattern or scheme which was adopted very early in life is maintained throughout, and every new experience is interpreted in terms of it; verifying it, as it were, and contributing to its rigidity. (1963, 49)

This danger was illustrated by Bacon in the following often-quoted anecdote:

> And therefore it was a good answer that was made by one who when they showed him hanging in a temple a picture of those who had paid their vows as having escaped shipwreck, and would have him say whether he did not now acknowledge the power of the gods, — "Aye," asked he again, "but where are they painted that were drowned after their vows?" (NO I, xlvi)

There is a natural inclination to stay inside the temple, so to speak, where negative instances of the theory connecting a safe voyage with paying one's vows are unlikely to present themselves. Bacon's advice, however, was to look elsewhere for counter-evidence.

A related tendency is where we stick to well-known and obvious effects in formulating and examining axioms, and ignore unusual and heterogeneous instances. Although a wide variety of instances do not appear spontaneously, they should nevertheless be deliberately sought, for they are of greater value in testing theories:

> The human understanding is moved by those things most which strike and enter the mind simultaneously and suddenly, and so fill the imagination; and then it feigns and supposes all other things to be somehow, though it cannot see how, similar to those few things by which it is surrounded. But for that going to and fro to remote and heterogeneous instances, by which axioms are tried as in the fire, the intellect is altogether slow and unfit, unless it be forced thereto by severe laws and overruling authority. (NO I, xlvii)

That heterogeneous instances enjoy a special advantage over similar and commonplace ones is a central (and very sensible) principle which Bacon said should guide the construction of competent histories, as we shall see in Chapter Six, when discussing this aspect of his philosophy.

Idols of the Cave also arise because of an "extreme admiration of antiquity", which affects some, and the "extreme love and appetite for novelty", to which others are given. Bacon recommended a middle course between these two extremes: we should not automatically carp at the achievements of the ancients, nor despise the work of the moderns, for "truth is to be sought for not in the felicity of any age, which is an unstable thing, but in the light of nature and experience, which is eternal" (NO I, lvi)

Another such idol arises from two distinct mental types that Bacon pointed out: "The steady and acute mind can fix its contemplations and dwell and fasten on the subtlest distinctions: the lofty and discursive mind recognises and puts together the finest and most general resemblances. Both kinds however easily err in excess, by catching the one at gradations the other at shadows". (NO I, lv) Though he did not draw any lesson explicitly from this aphorism, Bacon was presumably suggesting, as he did in several other places, that some middle way between the purely speculative and the purely empirical is to be preferred.

Bacon's central message in his discussion of these idols is fairly clear. It is to point out that pride in authorship, excessive respect for particular eras, and other individual proclivities may cause axioms to be adopted without the proper scientific, critical procedures being respected. Hence his wise concluding advice:

BACON	POPPER
And generally let every student of nature take this as a rule,— that whatever his mind seizes and dwells upon with peculiar satisfaction is to be held in suspicion, and that so much the more care is to be taken in dealing with such questions to keep the understanding even and clear. (NO I, lviii)	in searching for the truth, it may be our best plan to start by criticizing our most cherished beliefs. (1963, 6)

The idol of the Tribe on which Bacon laid particular stress, as being "by far the greatest hindrance and aberration of the human understanding", proceeded, he believed, "from the dulness, incompetency, and deceptions of the sense". It could be thought that Bacon was here lamenting and seeking to make up for the inability of the unaided senses to make infallible judgements. This fits in with the idea that he repudiated speculation and wished to build an infallible science on a foundation of infallible facts. That is, for instance, the way Richard Popkin read Bacon:

[Bacon believed that] a set of conditions can be given, in terms of corrections of the unaided senses, which, when coupled with certain internal reforms, will specify when our adjusted perceptions are veridical. (1964, 129)

But Bacon's complaint about the senses, when considered in the context in which it was delivered, has a quite different complexion. His claim was not that we needed to mend or assist the senses in order to steer clear of uncertainty and speculation. Quite the contrary. Bacon's regret was that, because the fundamental constituents of nature are imperceptible, we are inclined, to the great detriment of science, not to speculate about

them at all. As the reader will recall, it was this kind of
speculation, which reaches "beneath the surface" and into the
"inner and further recesses of nature" (NO I, xviii), that Bacon
wished to encourage as part of the interpretation of nature.
Consider now what Bacon said:

> But by far the greatest hindrance and aberration of the
> human understanding proceeds from the dulness,
> incompetency, and deceptions of the senses; in that things
> which strike the sense outweigh things which do not
> immediately strike it, though they be more important. *Hence
> it is that speculation commonly ceases where sight ceases;
> insomuch that of things invisible there is little or no
> observation.* Hence all the working of the spirits inclosed in
> tangible bodies lies hid and unobserved of men. So also all
> the more subtle changes of form in the parts of coarser
> substances . . . is in like manner unobserved. And yet unless
> these two things just mentioned be searched out and brought
> to light, nothing great can be achieved in nature, as far as the
> production of works is concerned. So again the essential
> nature of our common air, and of all bodies less dense than
> air (which are very many), is almost unknown. For the sense
> by itself is a thing infirm and erring; *neither can instruments
> for enlarging or sharpening the senses do much;* but all the
> truer kind of interpretation of nature is effected by instances
> and experiments fit and apposite; wherein the sense decides
> touching the experiment only, and the experiment touching
> the point in nature and the thing itself. (NO I, 1; my italics)

Bacon's idea here is, I think, fairly clear, and it is in line with the
interpretation I am proposing. The senses, even if assisted by
instruments, cannot perceive those minute and internal processes
which underlie nature, and this has made people reluctant to
speculate on those processes. The interpretation of nature,
however, requires that we discover how they operate. But this
does not mean that the senses are called upon to achieve
impossible feats of perception. As Bacon said (and, incidentally,
repeated several times in his works), "the sense decides touching
the experiment only, and the experiment touching the point in
nature". If I understand him correctly, Bacon held that axioms

advanced in the course of interpreting nature will typically describe hidden and unobservable processes and phenomena. Those axioms, however, have observable empirical implications and it is by means of these that they are tested and confirmed. Knowledge of nature's internal mechanisms is thus derived indirectly, the role of the senses in the process being simply to report the results of experiments. It seems difficult to fault this account.

4(iii) The Idols of the Market-place

The third set of idols, those of the *Market-place*, "have crept into the understanding through the alliance of words and names" (NO I, lix). The problem Bacon saw here is that, by employing certain words and expressions, we frequently become committed unawares to corresponding theories: "For men believe that their reason governs words; but it is also true that words react on the understanding". The theories insinuated by words have, moreover, often not been through the scientific mill: "being commonly framed and applied according to the capacity of the vulgar, [they] follow those lines of division which are most obvious to the vulgar understanding. And whenever an understanding of greater acuteness or a more diligent observation would alter those lines to suit the true divisions of nature, words stand in the way and resist the change." That is to say, attempts to correct common assumptions are frustrated by the unreflecting use of those words in which they are embedded.

Examples of contemporary relevance, which might illustrate Bacon's thesis, are certain terms connected with feelings and thought that traditionally applied just to human beings and sometimes to animals, whence to say of a machine that it is in pain or that it reasons intelligently has appeared to many philosophers to be blatantly self-contradictory. The theory behind this usage is that consciousness is necessarily connected with some characteristic of living creatures, which machines could never possess. And because the usage is so widespread, challenging the corresponding theory is more difficult than it would otherwise have been. This much of Bacon's analysis is surely right.

Bacon originally thought that this difficulty could be mastered by proceeding in the mathematical fashion of "setting down in the very beginning the definitions of our words and terms, that others may know how we accept and understand them" (AL, 397). But in the later version of the discussion, in the *Novum Organum*, Bacon judged that this would not do, "since the definitions themselves consist of words, and those words beget others"; that is to say, a rule requiring all the terms of a debate to be defined at the outset would be ineffectual, for it would lead to an infinite regress of definitions. (NO I, lix) Bacon said that this difficulty makes it necessary to employ his inductive scheme and, in particular, "to recur to individual instances, and those in due series and order". But it is hard to see how the problem posed by the theoretical presuppositions of words could be solved by such means, for the observed instances need to be expressed before they can be employed; and how can they be expressed if not in words?

Some terms that impose their theoretical presuppositions illegitimately on the understanding do so by being treated as names which, however, have no real objects to which they refer. Bacon instanced the expressions "fortune", "prime mover", "planetary orbits", and "element of fire" as "fictions which owe their origin to false and groundless *(vanis)* theories." The problems posed by such words are not so difficult to dispel, however, "because to get rid of them it is only necessary that the theories [or, perhaps, just "theories"—*theoriarum*] should be steadily rejected and dismissed as obsolete." (NO I, lx) I assume that the theories in question that Bacon wished to dislodge are the false and groundless ones which he mentioned in the concluding phrase of the preceding sentence as being the source of the difficulty. This assumption is, however, contradicted by Ellis and Spedding, who translated *theoriarum* as "*all* theories" (my italics), thus strongly endorsing the standard view of Bacon's

attitude to theories in general. I suggest, though, that their
translation is not warranted; certainly no other translation of the
Novum Organum that I have seen agrees with Ellis's and
Spedding's rendering of this passage.*

Another difficulty presented by words "springs out of a faulty
and unskilful abstraction, [and] is intricate and deeply rooted"
(NO I, lx). Bacon exemplified his (not altogether clear) point with
the word 'humid', which he regarded as "a mark loosely and
confusedly applied to denote a variety of actions which will not
bear to be reduced to any constant meaning." The numerous
different meanings that the word carried meant that "when you
come to apply the word, — if you take it in one sense, flame is
humid; if in another, air is not humid; if in another, fine dust is
humid; if in another, glass is humid. So that it is easy to see that
the notion is taken by abstraction only from water and common
and ordinary liquids, without any due verification." (NO I, lx)

Bacon was not very explicit about what particular difficulty was
posed by the ambiguity of a word like 'humid'. If mutual
understanding were the problem, it could surely be solved by
inventing different terms for the word's various uses ($humid_1$,
$humid_2$, etc.). There seems no reason why Bacon should not have
accepted this as a way of avoiding mutual incomprehension;
however, he might also have been concerned lest the device give
the false impression that phenomena that naturally belong
together were heterogeneous, or that those that have no real
affinity were of the same kind. For, as we shall see in Chapter Six,
Bacon did give some sign of believing what many philosophers
now believe (thought I cannot accept the idea), that certain
phenomena bear an essential similarity to one another, while
others are essentially different. Similar phenomena are then said
to belong to separate 'natural kinds'. Given this theory, the
groupings induced by our names can, in a sense, be either right

---

*The relevant Latin passage reads as follows: Prioris generis sunt Fortuna, Primum
Mobile, Planetarum Orbes, Elementum Ignis, et hujusmodi commenta, quae a vanis et
falsis theoriis ortum habent. Atque hoc genus Idolorum facilius ejicitur, quia per
constantem abnegationem et antiquationem theoriarum exterminari possunt.

or wrong, depending on whether or not they match the natural kinds.

This may account for Bacon's insistence that the correct meaning and use of terms needed to be settled by experiment and induction, for this is the only process that could discover the natural kinds. A second reason may derive from Bacon's view that a proper induction not only leads to a true causal analysis but also clarifies terms. There is, indeed, a good deal of truth in this thesis. Investigations often start out with a rather hazy notion of the subject-matter being researched but, as discoveries accumulate, this notion is refined and made more precise. Bacon's own study of the nature of heat bears this out. As we shall see in Chapter Six, where we examine it in detail, Bacon began with a vague and subjective conception of heat which he would have been unable to define, and ended up with a relatively precise definition, expressed in terms of the motion of the minute parts of matter.

It is reasonable to assume, too, that terms may vary in precision and, given the theory of natural kinds, in how closely they approximate to the postulated natural classification. If so, one could explain the remarks with which Bacon concluded his discussion of the idols of the Market-place. He said that "There are however in words certain *degrees* of distortion and error" and that "some notions are of necessity a little better than others, in proportion to the greater variety of subjects that fall within the range of the human sense" (NO I, lx; my italics) Bacon reckoned that words describing qualities were often the "most faulty", mentioning as examples 'heavy', 'light', 'rare', and 'dense', all of which were subjected to a more or less thorough empirical investigation by Bacon himself.

4(iv) The Idols of the Theatre

The last set of idols comprises a variety of closely related attitudes arising from faulty philosophical systems, whose specious plausibility Bacon compared with that of stage-plays, and

from "perverse rules *(perversis legibus)* of demonstration". Bacon
divided them into three classes: the Rational, the Empirical, and
the Superstitious.

The most conspicuous representative of the first class was
Aristotle, "who corrupted natural philosophy by his logic:
fashioning the world out of categories" (NO I, lxiii). Although
Aristotle may, by referring to a multitude of observations, *appear*
to have employed the correct experimental method, closer
examination shows this to have been a sham:

> For he had come to his conclusion before; he did not consult
> experience, as he should have done, in order to the framing
> of his decisions and axioms; but having first determined the
> question according to his will, he then resorts to experience,
> and bending her into conformity with his placets leads her
> about like a captive in a procession . . . (NO I, lxiii)

We should, therefore, not be deceived by Aristotle's frequent
allusions to observations, for it

> comes too late, after his mind was made up. His practice was
> not to seek information from unfettered experiment but to
> exhibit experience captive and bound. He did not introduce a
> wide impartial survey of experience to assist his investigation
> of truth; he brought in a carefully schooled and selected
> experience to justify his pronouncements. (RP, 130)

Without entering into any controversy as to whether this is a just
indictment of Aristotle, which is hard to do anyway, since Bacon
did not specify to which particular theories he objected, we
should admit that Bacon's observation is an acute one. Even if a
theory is presented along with a mass of supporting data, we
should be alert to the possibility that the evidence has been
carefully screened and selected, so as to present the theory in the
best light.

The second idol of the Theatre is termed Empirical: "it has its
foundations . . . in the narrowness and darkness of a few
experiments" (NO I, lxiv), from which the empiric "fabricates a
complete system" (RP, 122). Bacon cited two representatives of

this particular fault, namely, William Gilbert, whose famous book, *De Magnete,* had been published in 1600, and the traditional alchemists, all of whom he charged with trying to build a ship out of a single plank (RP, 122). In due course, we shall discuss more specifically what Bacon objected to in Gilbert, as this is a controversial matter. It is less difficult to descry alchemy's objectionable theoretical structure: this comprised the doctrines of man as a microcosm of the universe; the idea that the world is composed of four elements, air, fire, earth and water; and the so-called 'matrices', mercury, sulphur, arsenic and salt, all of which Bacon described as a "fanciful construction" and of which he said: "I do not think any genuine natural philosopher would admit even into his dreams such an arbitrary ordering of nature." (RP, 122)

At least in regard to alchemy, Bacon's judgment can hardly be faulted, for the limited scope of alchemical observations simply could not justify the extravagant speculations mentioned above; the natural and "premature hurry of the understanding" does indeed need to be curbed.

The Rational and Empirical idols each misuse the results of experiments, though in different ways. The first makes a careful but biased selection from a large stock of relevant data, in order to advance some fixed and preconceived idea. The second erects a vast speculation on a too limited range of experiments. Bacon compared these activities to the work of the spider and the ant, and he urged that we ought instead to take our lead from the bee, who might well have adopted the Bacon family motto—*Mediocria Firma*—:

> Those who have handled sciences have been either men of
> experiment or men of dogmas. The men of experiment are
> like the ant; they only collect and use: the reasoners
> resemble spiders, who make cobwebs out of their own
> substance. But the bee takes a middle course; it gathers
> its material from the flowers of the garden and of the field,
> but transforms and digests it by a power of its own. Not
> unlike this is the true business of philosophy; for it neither
> relies solely or chiefly on the powers of the mind, nor does it

take the matter which it gathers from natural history and
mechanical experiments and lay it up in the memory whole,
as it finds it; but lays it up in the understanding altered
and digested. Therefore from a closer and purer league
between these two faculties, the experimental and the
rational, (such as has never yet been made) much may be
hoped. (NO I, xcv)

4(v) The Idols of Superstition

4(v a) Science and Superstition.   The third idol of the Theatre
corrupts philosophy "by superstition and an admixture of
theology" (NO I, lxv). Bacon took little trouble to explain
precisely what he meant by superstition but it is clear from
various scattered remarks that it was either a straightforwardly
heretical belief or else a religious attitude or doctrine not
sanctioned by the Scriptures. For instance, he called superstition
one of "the extremes of religion", the other being infidelity
(*Filium Labyrinthi, Works* III, 501). And elsewhere he described
it in the following terms:

> Superstition, rejecting the light of the Scriptures, and
> giving itself up to corrupt or apocryphal traditions, and
> new revelations or false interpretations of the Scriptures,
> invents and dreams many things concerning the will of
> God which are astray and alien from the Scriptures.
> (*Of Heresies, Works* VII, 252–3)

> As the likeness of an ape to a man makes him all the
> more ugly, so does the likeness of superstition to religion.
> (DA 6iii, 477–8)

Bacon's most interesting criticism of superstition was not,
however, aroused by its heterodoxy (which is a poor objection); it
was that superstitious doctrines were established and maintained
by the kind of dogmatical and unscientific reasoning which he had

frequently condemned, especially under the heads of the first two sets of idols. Thus he judged "the general root of superstition" to be that "men observe when things hit and not when they miss; and commit to memory the one, and forget and pass over the other" (*Sylva*, 668). And this objection is presented clearly in his essay "On Superstition", where he compared the manner in which superstitions were treated and defended to the instrumentalism that operated in traditional astronomy:

> The master of superstition is the people; and in all superstition wise men follow fools; and arguments are fitted to practice, in a reversed order. It was gravely said by some of the prelates in the council of Trent, where the doctrine of the schoolmen bare great sway, *that the schoolmen were like astronomers, which did feign eccentrics and epicycles, and such engines of orbs, to save the phaenomena; though they knew there were no such things;* and in like manner, that the schoolmen had framed a number of subtle and intricate axioms and theorems, to save the practice of the church. (*Works* VI, 416)

The advance of learning was also hindered by the overzealous religiosity exemplified by certain theologians of Bacon's day, who discouraged research in the belief that the injunction "against those who pry into sacred mysteries" extends to "the hidden things of nature" (NO I, lxxxix). Bacon, however, insisted that the second sort of inquiry was barred by no such religious prohibition. Others were apprehensive lest a knowledge of the physical causes of things should threaten the authority of religion. In Bacon's view, no such conflict should arise between science and religion; on the contrary, "if the matter be truly considered, natural philosophy is after the word of God at once the surest medicine against superstition, and the most approved nourishment for faith, and therefore she is rightly given to religion as her most faithful handmaid, since the one displays the will of God, the other his power." (NO I, lxxxix)

Thus, far from undermining the claims of religion, natural philosophy, properly cultivated, corroborates them. For while it is true that "a little philosophy inclineth man's mind to atheism", "depth in philosophy bringeth men's minds about to religion" ("Of Atheism"). Bacon's idea was that a superficial knowledge of a variety of separate fields may excite no particular wonder, but a deeper understanding of the multiplicity of things and the intricate connexions between them will demand an explanation that only an appeal to the Deity can supply:

> For while the mind of man looketh upon second causes scattered, it may sometimes rest in them, and go no further; but when it beholdeth the chain of them, confederate and linked together, it must needs fly to Providence and Deity. Nay, even that school which is most accused of atheism doth most demonstrate religion; that is, the school of Leucippus and Democritus and Epicurus. For it is a thousand times more credible, that four mutable elements, and one immutable fifth essence, duly and eternally placed, need no God, than that an army of infinite small portions or seeds unplaced, should have produced this order and beauty without a devine marshal. ("Of Atheism" *Works* VI, 413)

4(v b) Final Causes.   In ancient times, another kind of superstitious reverence engendered the idea in the minds of some natural philosophers that inquiries into physical causes were inferior to the more lofty study of abstract forms, first causes, and final causes (NO I, lxv). Bacon devoted only a little space to criticizing abstract and first causes, though the former, which he connected with Plato, were named as one of the reasons for the fruitlessness of that philosopher's work, its use of too limited a range of experience being the other. (RP, 115) Most of Bacon's fire was aimed at final causes, which he also mentioned among the idols of the Tribe.

The attack on final causes drew a good deal of attention, most of it favourable, from later philosophers, though some, I believe, have misunderstood Bacon's message. For example, according to Lord Brougham (1856, 96), Bacon "excluded Final Causes . . . as a preposterous speculation—an irreverent attempt to penetrate mysteries hidden from human eyes by the imperfection of our nature." But Bacon did not call these causes into question for being preposterous (i.e., plainly false), nor was he primarily concerned that they strayed into the forbidden territory of divinity, though there is undoubtedly an element of this in his objection. Explanations such as "the clouds are formed above for watering the earth" and "a tree's leaves are for protecting the fruit from the sun and wind" are inappropriate in natural philosophy, Bacon said,

> not because those final causes are not true and worthy to be inquired in metaphysical speculations; but because their excursions and irruptions into the limits of physical causes *has bred a waste and solitude in that track.* (DA 3iv, 364; my italics)

And elsewhere he said that the handling of final causes tends "to the great arrest and prejudice of further discovery" (AL, 358), unlike physical causes, which "give light and direction to new inventions" (DA 3iv, 362). If Bacon could have shown that final causes are *necessarily* incapable of leading to new discoveries, his attack would have been a more powerful one and in keeping with his general methodology. However, he simply took this for granted, being guided by the sterile examples he found in Aristotle.

Bacon is sometimes criticized for not noticing that final causes could and would, in a couple of centuries, be employed very usefully in biology—Thorndike, for instance, sarcastically remarking that his "criticism perhaps accords none too well with the doctrine of evolution and survival of the fittest" (1958, 67). Against this, it seems rather trifling to object that Bacon failed to predict what nobody before Darwin managed to anticipate. But in any case, although teleological or functional explanations have secured a place in modern biology, their precise import and manner of operation are far from uncontroversial. Had Bacon been confronted with the modern equivalent of final causes, I suspect he would have followed the line that Carl Hempel takes.

That is, he would have interpreted them as merely a species of ordinary causal explanation, which do not really rely on what he considered to be genuine final causes—these being essentially connected with a conscious purpose, either God's purpose or that of a human mind. Thus he praised Democritus as one "who removed God and Mind from the structure of things . . . and assigned the causes of particular things to the necessity of matter, without any intermixture of final causes". (DA 3iv, 363–4)

4(v c) *Science and Religion.*   The last of the idols of the Theatre occurs when science is combined with theology, whereby both are seen as similar sorts of discipline. Such a union results in the arrest of scientific development, as had occurred, for instance, when certain divines incorporated the philosophy of Aristotle into theology and "fashioned it into the shape of an art" (NO I, lxxxix), an expression which Bacon frequently employed to describe a closed and completed system to which no alternative could be contemplated nor any addition made. He levelled the same complaint in the *Thoughts and Conclusions* (p. 78): when philosophy and theology, he said, form an "intimate contract [in which] only what is already received in Natural Philosophy is included; all fresh growth, additions, improvements are excluded more strictly and obstinately than ever before." And he concluded that when science and theology are confounded, "every development of philosophy, every new frontier and direction, is regarded by religion with unworthy suspicion and violent contempt."

Another danger that may come from uniting theology and science is that, by drawing on the Bible for physical facts and laws, "there arises not only a fantastic philosophy but also an heretical religion." (NO I, lxv) Bacon exemplified the first of these dangers with the fantastic philosophy produced by "some of the moderns" who had "indulged so far as to attempt to found a system of natural philosophy on the first chapter of Genesis, on the book of Job, and other parts of the sacred writings" (NO I, lxv), a "distemper" that Bacon traced to "the Rabbis and

Cabbalists", but which he noted particularly in the school of
Paracelsus (DA 9i, 117, and MBT, 66). Although Bacon
volunteered no specific examples here, it is certainly true that
many Paracelcians looked to the Scriptures as a source-book for
their physical speculations, using them as a guide to the number
and nature of the elements, and the structure of the cosmos. (See
Debus, 1966, ch. 3.) Bacon perceived a greater danger from this
"ill-matched union" between science and religion than from open
hostility (TC, 78) and he urged that a clear separation be effected,
in which we "give to faith that only which is faith's" (NO I, lxv).

At first sight, it is rather perplexing that Bacon should have
banished the Bible as a source of information for the scientist.
After all, he professed an earnest faith in the Scriptures and in the
articles of Christianity; one would have thought that if they were
true, then their incorporation into natural philosophy would be
welcomed. One suggested answer is that Bacon's religion might
not have been sincerely held, that he hid his real beliefs, merely
making an outward show of piety for political reasons. However,
this is highly implausible, in view of the frequency of his pious
declarations and the number of explicitly religious works which he
penned.* More tellingly though, if he had been keen to hide his
supposed atheism, he would hardly have risked taking so definite
and public a stand against mixing religion and science.

As a matter of fact, Bacon explained and justified his desire to
effect a division between science and religion with some care, the
key to his view being that, although he believed sincerely in
certain fundamental tenets of his religion, he was no
fundamentalist. Thus he tells us that the Scriptures, while

---

*Bacon wrote a "Confession of Faith", and three or four "Prayers", which were first printed
in 1648; a work entitled "Religious Meditations", printed with the *Essays* in 1597; and
translations of several psalms, that first appeared in print in 1625. A piece called "The
Christian Paradoxes", first printed in 1645, which lists a number of "paradoxes and seeming
contradictions" that a Christian is called upon to believe, has struck some as an atheist's
satire. However, Grosart, in 1865, demonstrated conclusively that Bacon was not
responsible for the work, and that it was, in fact, composed by the theologian Herbert
Palmer.

divinely inspired, are dishonoured when they are expounded "in the same way as human writings". A literal interpretation would be misleading, for the Scriptures "are written to the hearts of men, and comprehend the vicissitudes of all ages". Consequently,

> they are not to be interpreted only according to the latitude
> and obvious sense of the place; or with respect to the
> occasion whereon the words were uttered; or in precise
> context with the words before or after; or in contemplation of
> the principal scope of the passage; but we must consider
> them to have in themselves, not only totally or collectively,
> but distributively also in clauses and words, infinite springs
> and streams of doctrines. (DA 9i, 117)

Biblical exegesis would also benefit if this were accepted, for it opens the way to solving a number of difficulties, such as the apparent irrelevance of Christ's replies to some of his questioners. This could be understood, Bacon maintained, if it were appreciated that Christ was addressing the inner thoughts of his listeners and was speaking more generally "to men of every age and nation"; hence we cannot take his words in their literal and obvious sense. Bacon's view, then, was that since the Scriptures are largely metaphorical, they provide an unreliable source of information on physical principles. This explains his warning that a "fantastic philosophy" would be produced if science and religion were confounded.

The second danger that Bacon saw in reading the Book of God as if it were the Book of Nature was that an "heretical religion" might result. His reasoning seems to have been as follows: Bacon took the Scriptures as having a central core of tenets, which he called the "sacred" or "divine mysteries" and about which we could not speculate with profit or piety, such matters as the will of God and the character of the Trinity being included here. These mysteries seem to be ideas which are not comprehensible in the normal way and which should not be inquired into too curiously, as for instance when Nicodemus asked, "How can a man be born when he is old?" With such mysteries, we simply have to knuckle under, as it were. God has helped "by so expressing his mysteries

that they may be most sensible to us; and by grafting his
revelations upon the notions and conceptions of our reason; and
by applying his inspirations to open our understanding, as the
form of the key to the ward of the lock." (DA 9i, 114)

Not every idea is open to debate, then. Some things are
hidden from ordinary investigation and can be comprehended
only through divine revelation: "the articles and principles of
religion [are] . . . completely exempted from the examination of
reason" (DA 9i, 114). These articles and principles, however, seem
to have been few and rather vague; they concerned God's will
primarily, which Bacon was wise enough not to specify in any
detail. And he never faced the problem of how to distinguish in
the Scriptures those literal truths from that which is intended to
be merely metaphorical.

4(vi) Summary

The idols constitute an important part of Bacon's philosophy,
further illustrating and explaining his conception of the methods
by which science should be advanced and his theory of why they
have, in fact, advanced so little. The damaging mental dispositions
represented by the idols closely match the faults that Bacon
picked out in the method of anticipation. This is seen in those
tendencies, which an overfondness for a particular theory
produces, to count evidence when it is in agreement with the
theory but not to seek evidence that might go against it; and when
facts which tell against the theory do surface, the policy is to
ignore them or to mould them into conformity with the theory by
means of appropriate distinctions. This uncritical attitude to
theories is particularly troublesome when those theories are
adopted unconsciously, as it were, by being incorporated into our
language.

The other aspects of anticipations, which we discussed earlier,
namely their tendency to erect extravagant speculations on too
small and unvaried an empirical base and to restrict speculations

to surface phenomena, also have their counterparts in the idols. The first corresponds to the empirical idols, and the second is cited as one of the idols of the Cave and is also reflected in the natural preference for final causes, rather than real, physical causes. Finally, Bacon's famous precept not to mix religion and science was founded, not on atheism, but, principally, on what he thought was the unreliability of the Scriptures as a source of physical information, though he never expressed a doubt about their divine inspiration.

Many of the tendencies to which Bacon pointed are, I think, real threats to science and it is remarkable that he noticed them, and saw them as faults, at a time when there was so little science to go on. Bacon's achievement is the more striking when we see some of the same points advanced in the present day as if they were novel.

Chapter Five
Bacon's Assessment of the Science of His Day

All the philosophy of nature
which is now received, is either
the philosophy of the Grecians,
or that other of the alchemists.
. . . The one never faileth to
multiply words, and the other
ever faileth to multiply gold. (In
Praise of Knowledge)

5(i) Introduction

Bacon's preoccupation with what science ought to be like led him to address the question of how science had in fact been conducted in the past, for he wished to show the poverty of established methods of induction and to illustrate how they could be improved. Hence, he thought it would be "good to make some pause upon that which is received; that thereby the old may be more easily made perfect and the new more easily approached" (*Plan*, 22). The resulting historical survey is interesting particularly for the light it sheds on the new methods which Bacon was advancing.

In the eyes of many observers, Bacon's "coasting voyage along the shores of the arts and sciences received" (*Plan*, 22) was not an entirely successful trip, and it has done considerable injury to his reputation as a judge of what is of scientific value. For he has seemed to come down too often on the wrong side—against Gilbert and Copernicus, for example, and (it is claimed) in opposition to mathematics in science—and, what is worse, for the wrong reasons. These alleged misjudgments have, moreover, appeared all the more discreditable in view of the tactless and strident manner in which he excoriated scientists whose work he is supposed barely to have understood. Thus Bertrand Russell, in a rather extreme statement of this view, said:

> When it came to science, Bacon was wrong on almost every point. The great discoveries of his contemporaries were almost all rejected by him—even the circulation of the blood, discovered by his own physician—and certainly were not made in accordance with his precepts for inductive reasoning (1969, 163).

Bacon has also sometimes been criticized for making no important scientific discoveries himself, "despite all his grandiloquent claims" (Cohen, 1949, 101). I think this is slightly unfair to Bacon, for he did advance the scientific understanding of heat and of gravity, as we shall see. But in any case, we should not reproach a methodology for having been devised by someone who is not also a brilliant scientist; it must be assessed on its own terms, and not be dealt with ad hominem.

It is often said that Bacon misjudged the various sciences because of a misguided insistence that they should have no truck with hypotheses, but should be rigorously, that is, logically, established from a comprehensive set of data; and this sort of reasoning is, of course, all of a piece with the standard interpretation of his philosophy. I shall argue, on the other hand, that Bacon's appraisal of science did not, in fact, derive from a dislike of speculation; that his judgments were far sounder than Russell and many others have alleged; and that his reasoning was decided by the hypothetico-inductive methodology which I have suggested he always held.

5(ii) William Gilbert and Magnetism

Bacon has frequently been taken to task for his adverse
assessment of William Gilbert (1544–1603). Gilbert is justly
credited with being among the first modern experimenters; the
revolutionary discoveries he made in electricity and magnetism
were published in his *De Magnete* in 1600 and they were well-
known in the early seventeenth century. Yet far from singing
Gilbert's praises as the person who came nearest to practising a
correct inductive method, Bacon lumped him together with the
alchemists and condemned his "magnetic philosophy" in striking
terms. Bacon's judgment seems so perverse that it has been seen
by some as due to a jealousy of Gilbert's scientific success. Others
have argued that it reveals his own philosophy to have been
completely misconceived. It has even given rise to questions
about Bacon's "mental strength" (Benjamin, 1895, 317).

One explanation which has been canvassed is that, when
praising Gilbert, Bacon had his *De Magnete* in mind, while his
criticisms were inspired by an inferior and much less empirical
work, the *De Mundo Nostro Sublunari Philosophia Nova* (On our
Sublunary World, A New Philosophy). This book was not printed
until 1657, having been left incomplete by Gilbert. His brother,
also called William, collected the papers together after his death
and dedicated them to Prince Henry (1594-1612), to whom the
manuscript was presented, the most probable date of the
presentation being 1607 or 1608, according to Kelley's calculation
(1965, 9–16). Evidently some copies were made at about this time,
one or two of which found their way into Bacon's possession, and
the version which was eventually published came from Bacon's
library. However, this book has never been republished, being
generally regarded as a poor work, and the idea that it, rather
than the *De Magnete,* was the object of Bacon's attack is thus an
attractive option, which could extricate him from what otherwise
seems like an embarrassing misjudgment. Marie Boas (1951, 467)
even went so far as to argue that "Bacon had never read the *De
magnete* but based his opinion of Gilbert entirely upon the purely

speculative *Philosophia nova*", though the first part of this claim
has been completely discredited by Roller (1953). Carl Boyer
(1952, 419), after reviewing Gilbert's discussion of the causes of the
rainbow in the *Philosophia Nova*, "the infelicity . . . [of which]
must be admitted by his most sedulous admirers", also remarked
that the inferiority of this work "makes it less difficult for one to
appreciate the strictures which Francis Bacon . . . passed on the
writings of his brilliant countryman" (ibid., 420).

However, I think it unlikely that Bacon's criticisms of his
countryman were directed against the *Philosophia Nova*. For one
thing, this would have been a rather pointless (not to mention,
underhand) way of proceeding, since practically nobody else had
heard of that work, let alone read it. Secondly, Bacon's first
criticism was published in 1605, well before he could have had
access to Gilbert's manuscript, and the nature of that criticism
seems not to have been altered substantially by a reading of the
Philosophia Nova; it remained essentially unchanged throughout
his later writings.

The view I shall defend is that Bacon's criticism of Gilbert
referred to the *De Magnete*. And I shall also argue that we need
reproach neither Bacon nor his philosophy, for his appraisal of his
countryman was, for the most part, shrewd and accurate. It is
perhaps a rather dangerous undertaking to join Bacon's attack on a
work which enjoys the fame and distinction of the *De Magnete*,
"as remarkable for its scientific spirit as for its content" (Taylor,
1939, 147). But, as Boyer (1952, 416) remarked nicely, in connexion
with Gilbert, "a well-launched reputation all too easily grows
beyond the limits of sober valuation": I think Gilbert's wonderful
contributions to the science of magnetism and electricity have led
some scholars to pass over the few shortcomings of his work,
which for Bacon loomed large. As we shall see, some
contemporary admirers of Gilbert expressed misgivings similar to
Bacon's over the more extravagant parts of the *De Magnete*.

Bacon's first reference to Gilbert appeared in 1605, in the
Advancement of Learning, where he is associated with men who

have used to infect their meditations, opinions, and
doctrines, with some conceits which they have most admired,
or some sciences which they have most applied; and given all
things else a tincture according to them, utterly untrue and
unproper. (AL, 292–3)

Gilbert is then accused of having "made a philosophy out of the
observations of a loadstone", just as the alchemists "made a
philosophy out of a few experiments of the furnace".

Gilbert's ideas were also touched on and criticized in the
Thoughts and Conclusions of around 1607. In this work, Bacon
started out by praising Gilbert for having experimented to great
effect on the magnet, but then proceeded to attack him for
overbuilding on what Bacon seems to have regarded as too narrow
a foundation:

Then our fellow-countryman, Gilbert, having displayed great
steadiness and constancy of judgment in his painstaking
investigation of the magnet and deployed a great retinue, nay,
an army of experiments in support, promptly threatened the
foundation of a new sect in Natural Philosophy. He should
have been warned by the fate of Xenophanes, to whose
opinion he inclined; for his name was turned to ridicule.
(TC, 85)

Although *Thoughts and Conclusions* was not published by Bacon,
this is a view he continued to uphold. It recurred many years
later, for instance in the *Novum Organum*:

The race of chemists again out of a few experiments of the
furnace have built up a fantastic philosophy, framed with
reference to a few things; and Gilbert also, after he had
employed himself most laboriously in the study and
observation of the loadstone, proceeded at once to construct
an entire system in accordance with his favourite subject.
(NO I, liv)

And elsewhere Bacon remarked of Gilbert that, while he has "not
unscientifically introduced the question of magnetic force", he has

"himself become a magnet; that is, he has ascribed too many things to that force, and built a ship out of a shell." (*Works* V, 202)

The broad nature of Bacon's complaint seems to have been that, although Gilbert had made many valuable experimental discoveries, he used them to erect a theoretical structure which they could not support. This kind of criticism, no doubt, fits in very well with the view of Bacon's ideal science as demanding an initial collection of data and as having no place for speculative hypotheses. Gilbert can then be seen to have met the first requirement of the ideal, but to have violated the second. Indeed, these animadversions against Gilbert might seem like good evidence for the view of Bacon's method which I am challenging, and this is how they are often taken. For example, R. F. Jones (1961, 52) understood Bacon to be complaining that "Gilbert let his mind go beyond his data" and A. R. Hall (1983, 193) remarks that Bacon was "inclined to distrust [theories] as too idiosyncratic and subjective, as with William Gilbert and his magnetic philosophy".

In my opinion, however, Bacon was not motivated by any such general distrust of theories; his main objections to Gilbert were, on the contrary, directed against specific failings of a particular hypothesis. Moreover, I think that, after reading the *De Magnete*, many modern readers would conclude that Bacon's appraisal of Gilbert was not unjustified. The main portion of this book contains a painstaking and impressive account of Gilbert's experiments on electricity and magnetism; it reports a multitude of original observations and discoveries and shows that many current theories and old wives' tales concerning magnets were refuted by his carefully planned experiments. This part of Gilbert's work seems to have earned Bacon's approval, for he often spoke of the skill with which Gilbert investigated the loadstone, and frequently drew on the *De Magnete* when constructing his own experimental histories. I share Harré's view (1965, 2) that the "entire system" and "fantastic philosophy" which Bacon attacked is contained in the sixth, and last, chapter of the *De Magnete*, in which Gilbert essayed a broader, philosophical or cosmological view, based on his discoveries in magnetism. This chapter seeks to establish two main hypotheses, first, that the earth is a magnet and secondly, and at much greater length, that it possesses a diurnal motion.

The first of these conclusions was drawn in what many have judged to be a model of scientific reasoning, Gilbert's case resting primarily on the remarkable similarities which he had discovered between the behaviour of magnetic needles in relation to the earth and the way they respond in the vicinity of a small magnetised sphere, or *terrella*. Gilbert's second hypothesis, which occupies by far the greater portion of the chapter, was, on the other hand, advanced by means of rather shoddy and ineffectual arguments, delivered in a blustering and somewhat abusive tone. I believe that Bacon's attack was made with the second hypothesis in his sights, rather than the first. If this is right, then Bacon would be largely exonerated from the charges of showing an ignorance of proper scientific reasoning in his discussion of Gilbert, and of harbouring a prejudice against any sort of speculation.

First, consider the possibility favoured by some philosophers that, in his criticism of Gilbert, Bacon was referring to the hypothesis of the earth's magnetism. There is certainly evidence that Bacon was rather sceptical about some aspects of Gilbert's hypothesis. In his book *On the Ebb and Flow of the Sea*, written around 1616, he commended

> the diligence of Gilbert [which] has discovered for us most
> truly that all earth and every nature (which we call terrestrial)
> that is not supple but rigid, and as he himself calls it robust,
> has a direction or verticity [i.e., magnetic polarity], latent
> indeed and yet revealing itself in many exquisite
> experiments, towards north and south. (*Works* V, 454)

Thus Bacon seems to have accepted that the earth as a whole acts as a magnet. Nevertheless, he denied that every part of the earth possessed magnetic powers, and he took it upon himself to "limit and correct" Gilbert's observations on the magnetism of terrestrial matter, "by confining the assertion to the exterior concretions about the surface of the earth, and not extending it to the interior". This is clearly directed against Gilbert's claim that the central core of the earth is a vast homogeneous magnet while the outer surface exhibits only a weak magnetism in some of its parts. Bacon objected that the idea

> that the earth is a magnet was a notion hastily taken up from a very light fancy; as it is impossible that things in the interior of the earth can be like any substance exposed to the eye of man; for with us all things are relaxed, wrought upon, and softened by the sun and heavenly bodies, so that they cannot correspond with things situated in a place where such a power does not penetrate . . . (*Works* V, 455)

Bacon rather overstated his case here, for he possessed no evidence that exposure to the sun and the heavenly bodies could influence the magnetic properties of terrestrial matter. And, in any case, Gilbert had used a very similar argument to explain why the exterior surface of the earth was, for the most part, *non-*magnetic. However, there is an element of truth in Bacon's criticism. For, while Gilbert marshalled a good deal of evidence to show that the earth acts as a magnet, that evidence was also consistent with some or all of the central core of the planet being non-magnetic.

When Bacon dealt with the question of terrestrial magnetism in the *Novum Organum,* he left to one side the question of how much of the earth was magnetic, merely mentioning Gilbert's view on the issue, and he expressed himself a little more guardedly on the question of whether the planet as whole acts as a magnet. However, he appears more or less reconciled to the idea. He first of all gave a very sketchy account of Gilbert's evidence for the earth's polarity, omitting the phenomenon of the dip of the magnetic needle, which Gilbert regarded as especially important evidence. He then, rather meanly, I think, judged that "these things, though well observed, do not quite prove what he asserts." Bacon finally suggested a crucial experiment which could, as he thought, prove it. In the experiment, a magnetic globe is to be set with its poles towards the east and west, and an unmagnetised iron needle allowed to rest for some days on the globe. The needle will align itself naturally with the magnetic poles of the globe.

> Now if it be found that the needle, on being removed from the magnet and placed on a pivot, either starts off at once to the north and south, or gradually turns in that direction, then the presence of the earth must be admitted as the cause . . . (NO II, xxxvi)

The experiment which Bacon proposed was so close to ones already reported by Gilbert that its result could hardly have been in doubt.

Since Bacon all but conceded the magnetic nature of the earth in the same work in which he was still very critical of the "entire system" that Gilbert had composed, it is unlikely that that particular doctrine was the main source of his dissatisfaction. This, as I have suggested, originated in Gilbert's adherence to the idea that the earth moves. Bacon often associated Gilbert with this view. For instance, he spoke of "Gilbert, and all those (except Copernicus) who believed that the earth was a planet and movable, and as it were one of the stars" (DIG, 515) and of "our countryman Gilbert, who revived the doctrines of Philolaus" (DA 3iv, 359–60). Philolaus was a presocratic philosopher associated with the idea of a non-static earth, Diogenes Laertius, for instance, writing of him as "the first to declare that the earth moves in a circle" (Hicks, 1925, II, 399); and Gilbert himself referred to Philolaus in that context (1600, 318). It is not so easy, however, to identify the physical theory to which Bacon was alluding, when, in the *Advancement of Learning* (p. 366), he spoke of Gilbert as one who "revived, with some alterations and demonstrations, the opinions of Xenophanes". As we have seen, Bacon also linked Gilbert with the presocratic philosopher Xenophanes in his *Thoughts and Conclusions*.

Xenophanes does not appear to have entertained the notion of a moving earth; his physical ideas were, briefly, that the sun is made of ignited clouds and is each day a new one; that the earth is infinite; that everything is made of earth and water; and that all things are periodically destroyed by floods. (See Kirk et al., 1983.) Diogenes Laertius added that Xenophanes "holds that there are four elements of existent things, and worlds unlimited in number but not overlapping [in time]." (The last words were inserted by Hicks, 1925, II, 427, in his translation, by way of interpretation.) None of these ideas seems to resemble any of Gilbert's opinions, not even those of the *Philosophia Nova* (to which Bacon, in any case, would have had no access at the time of his referring to Gilbert as a follower of Xenophanes); I can only imagine that Bacon was mistaken in his impression of Xenophanes. This surprising conclusion gains support from the fact that, when Bacon translated the *Advancement*, the reference to Xenophanes was dropped, and replaced, in the corresponding passage, by one to Philolaus, a change presumably introduced as a correction, rather than with the idea of alluding to another part of Gilbert's work. Therefore, it is very likely that even when Bacon criticized Gilbert for views he shared with Xenophanes, his object was the theory of the motion of the earth, that was more properly associated with Philolaus.

To summarise, I think it most probable that Bacon's severe criticisms of Gilbert grew out of the latter's arguments for the earth's diurnal motion. If this were accepted, then we would have no need to censure him for a poor appreciation of genuine scientific method because, as I shall show, Gilbert's case was extremely weak and his attempt to bring to bear his discoveries in magnetism upon the question of the earth's motion was a fiasco.

Gilbert claimed, in the *De Magnete* (p. 327), to arrive at his conclusions concerning the earth's diurnal motion "not with mere probability, but with certainty". The arguments he gave were in part traditional, and in part of his own devising and based on his idea of the earth as a magnet. One argument of the former kind is the following: if there were no terrestrial diurnal motion, then it must be that "the highest heaven and all those visible splendors of the fixed stars are swept round in this rapid headlong career". To Gilbert's mind, this was "not probable", first of all, because no one had ever demonstrated that the stars are all fixed on a single "adamantine" sphere; "nor is there any doubt" in Gilbert's mind that, in fact, the stars are ranged at various distances from the earth (*De Magnete*, 319). Secondly, the *primum mobile*, which had been thought necessary to force the supposed motion of the stars, is invisible; it is an absurdity "beneath derision" (*De Magnete*, 322) and accepted only by "weaklings", "simpletons and the unlearned". And finally, the *primum mobile*, or the structure of the stellar system, would be wrecked by so rapid a turning. It might be thought that such reasoning would apply equally to the earth, that it too would be torn apart by its motion. But Gilbert said that it would not be, as it moves in a manner which is natural and intrinsic to the earth, and also because there is nothing to hinder its motion, since the earth revolves in a void (*De Magnete*, 326) This argument could, of course, just as well be applied to the fixed stars, as indeed traditionally it had been. But Gilbert entirely overlooked the traditional claim that the stars are composed of a substance not subject to the same laws that govern terrestrial matter. Bacon would also have discounted this theory; but he at least provided cogent arguments to explain why it should be rejected. (I discuss these below, in the section dealing with Bacon's views on astronomy.)

To these well-worn arguments, Gilbert added his own. For instance, he claimed that the magnetic character of the earth makes it "fitted for circular movement" (*De Magnete*, 330–1), a notion he tried to establish in the following way. He explained that a small spherical loadstone floating in water, with its polar axis unnaturally constrained so that its north-seeking pole points south, will revolve about its centre until it is realigned north and south. He inferred that the same would be true of "the largest mountain of loadstone . . . were it to be set afloat on a wide stream", and that the "whole earth would act in the same way". (*De Magnete*, 331) This argument is rather far-fetched, for it by no means follows that the earth would return to its present alignment if displaced, merely because objects on the earth do so, for the magnetism of the terrestrial globe may be the cause of the motion of these objects. And of course this was just Gilbert's view, which he seems conveniently to drop for the moment. But, secondly, the argument is irrelevant to the issue of whether the earth possesses a diurnal motion, since it could at best establish that the earth maintains a fixed alignment. Gilbert's claim to have "proven that all true parts of the earth do move circularly, and that all magnetic bodies (when fitly arranged) are borne round in a circle" (*De Magnete*, 335), was clearly unfounded.

Another argument Gilbert invented is a kind of teleological one. He maintained that God provided the earth with its magnetic forces, forces which Gilbert described as "primarily animate" and as the "primary soul", in order that it "might, with steadfastness, take direction, and that the poles might be opposite, so that on them, as at the extremities of an axis, the movement of diurnal rotation might be performed" (*De Magnete*, 328–9). The idea that magnetism endows the earth with purpose and a soul is central to Gilbert's thought, and he devoted a whole section to putting this view forward. He deemed not only "the whole world animate" but held that "all globes, all stars, and this glorious earth, too, [are] . . . from the beginning by their own destinate souls governed" (*De Magnete*, 309). And it is because of its "astral magnetic mind" that the earth performs a diurnal rotation, for, if it did not, "the sun would ever hang with its constant light over a given part, and, by long tarrying there, would scorch the earth . . . and man would perish", while in "other parts all would be horror, and all things frozen stiff with intense cold" (*De Magnete*, 333). The same could, of course, be achieved if the heavens rotated and our planet remained still, but Gilbert intemperately dismissed the idea that they would do so, "simply for the earth's sake", as "a ridiculous supposition" (*De Magnete*, 334). However, he provided no evidence that the earth and stars enjoy so lively a mental life, and this example of a final cause in the service of a lost cause can only have reinforced Bacon's view of their sterility.

Gilbert derided the standard objections that the sea would be flung with great force in the direction of the motion and that the clouds would be left behind if the earth rotated; they are dismissed as "old-wives' imaginings and ravings of philosophasters" (*De Magnete*, 337), for, as he put it,

> These effluences [air, moisture, etc.] cohere [with the earth]
> through continuity of substance; and heavy bodies, too, are
> united to earth by their heaviness and advance with it . . .
> And, for this reason, the diurnal revolution of the earth
> does not sweep bodies along nor retard them . . .
> (*De Magnete*, 340–1)

To be told by Gilbert that materials do not separate when subjected to a force because they tend to stick together is not to be told much, however. It is true that he hinted that the natural attraction of heavy bodies to the earth has a magnetic cause, but even so, this magnetic factor could not explain the tendency of non-magnetic substances, such as the waters of the sea and the clouds, to cohere with the earth.

Gilbert also brought his magnetic philosophy to bear on other cosmological effects, notably on the very great constancy of the length of the day and the period of the moon, and on the fact that the mean distance of the moon from the earth's centre is about 29⅚ diameters of the earth, while a solar revolution of the moon in its orbit takes 29 days, 12 hours, 44 minutes. Gilbert accounted for this coincidence (as he reckoned it) by reference to his magnetic ideas:

> the earth rotates [in its diurnal motion] in the space of 24
> hours, even as the moon does in her monthly course, *by a
> magnetical compact of both,* the globes being impelled
> forward according to the ratio of their orbits . . . (*De
> Magnete*, 345).

But Gilbert made no effort to disclose the precise mechanism by which this compact operates to produce the result, nor is there anything ready at hand in his philosophy which would do the trick.

With this summary of Gilbert's cosmology in mind, it will perhaps be less surprising that he found no unqualified admirer in Bacon. Bacon's attack seems to have been targeted on the cosmology, in particular on the part involving the earth's mobility, which Gilbert imagined, quite wrongly, could be justified by his magnetic discoveries. Bacon was, it is true, more inclined to the idea of a stationary earth, as we shall discuss later, but there is no need to interpret his attitude either as blind prejudice or as a revulsion from speculation itself. Still less is it appropriate to infer, as many have done, that Bacon's judgment came out of jealousy or from an inability to understand Gilbert. Gilbert made numerous valuable discoveries in his experimental work, as Bacon readily acknowledged. He also argued well for his theory that the earth is a large magnet and here, too, Bacon (almost) gave him his due. But that the earth's magnetism could cause its diurnal motion, and that the earth and the planets are imbued with intelligence, were grossly implausible suppositions, unsupported by any evidence available to Gilbert. Bacon was right to object that in explaining the various cosmological phenomena by reference to terrestrial magnetism, Gilbert "ascribed too many things to that force".

Bacon was not alone in this assessment of Gilbert. William Barlow, an intimate friend of Gilbert's, while proclaiming that the magnetic nature of the earth, which Gilbert had discovered, was "the very true fountain of all magnetical knowledge", went on to disavow the cosmology of the last part of the *De Magnete*:

> But concerning his sixth book entreating of the motion of the earth, I think there is no man living farther from believing it, than myself, being nothing at all persuaded thereunto, by the reasons of other men, which he allegeth, and as little or less (if it were possible) by those his inventions, endeavouring to prove the motion of the earth by the earth's *magnetical* force and virtue. (Barlow, 1616, preface; I have modernised the orthography.)

This lack of enthusiasm for Gilbert's cosmology even surfaced in the "laudatory address" by Edward Wright which opens the *De Magnete*. Though Wright endorsed Gilbert's discovery "that the entire globe is magnetical" and held that it was so well buttressed and confirmed by apposite experiments "that no room is left for doubt or contradiction" (*De Magnete*, xl), he became positively defensive about Gilbert's views on the diurnal motion: "As for what you have finally to say of the circular motion of the earth and the terrestrial poles, *though many will deem it the merest theorizing*, still I do not see why it should not meet with indulgence . . . " (*De Magnete*, xli; my italics). Wright then listed a number of the standard arguments, and barely alluded to Gilbert's novel magnetical considerations. It seems very likely, then, that misgivings about Gilbert's cosmology were common, even amongst his admirers, and that the mixture of praise and censure with which Bacon greeted Gilbert was not out of the ordinary.

5(iii) Astrology

It is to Bacon's credit that he judged astrology on scientific and experimental grounds and not simply on whether its assumptions were consistent with some favourite metaphysical belief. One of the commonest criticisms of astrology in the sixteenth and seventeenth centuries, that it was unchristian, is not an objection to which Bacon resorted. Nor did he succumb to the dogma that the planets could never affect sublunary events. He regarded astrology as a legitimate science, which should be assessed in relation to the empirical evidence:

> for my part I admit astrology as a part of Physic, and yet attribute to it nothing more than is allowed by reason and the evidence of things, all fictions and superstitions being set aside. (DA 3iv, 349)

Bacon, for example, objected to the astrological doctrines of nativities, elections, and inquiries, that is, the beliefs that "the hour of nativity or conception influences the fortune of the birth, the hour of commencement the fortune of the enterprise, [and] the hour of inquiry the fortune of the thing inquired into", on the grounds that they "have in my judgment for the most part nothing sure or solid, *and are plainly refuted and convicted by physical reasons.*" (DA 3iv, 350; my italics)

Bacon did not present any more detailed analysis of the theories of astrology or cite refuting evidence, but failed astrological predictions were, presumably, familiar to many of his readers and did not need to be spelled out. As I have already mentioned, Bacon was fully alive to the fact that a theory which forms the basis of an unsuccessful prediction may not actually be to blame for that failure, and his most telling criticism of astrology, in the *Novum Organum*, was that its practitioners never did blame it. That is to say, astrology was a kind of anticipation of nature and illustrated the way in which one of the chief idols of the mind operates. Incidentally, Popper criticized astrology with similar arguments.

BACON	POPPER
And such is the way of all superstition, whether in astrology, dreams, omens, divine judgments, or the like; wherein men, having a delight in such vanities, mark the events where they are fulfilled, but where they fail, though this happen much oftener, neglect and pass them by. (NO I, xlvi)	Astrology did not pass the test [of scientificity]. Astrologers were greatly impressed, and misled, by what they believed to be confirming evidence—so much so that they were quite unimpressed by any unfavourable evidence. (1963, 37)

As we have seen before, one consequence of this unscientific procedure is that the whole world is somehow interpreted in the light of the theory—"the first conclusion colours and brings into conformity with itself all that come after" (NO I, xlvi)—and the theory acquires the false appearance of being strongly endorsed by a mass of evidence with which it is merely consistent. The above quotation also shows that Bacon levelled the same criticisms against other kinds of divination popular in his time, in which soothsayers professed to see portents of the future in dreams and in remarkable events. Here, too, he did not join the usual kind of debate, and biblical citation, over whether God would place omens in dreams.

Bacon also rejected a principal argument used in support of the casting of horoscopes:

> [Astrologers] say that as experience proves that the solstices, equinoxes, new moons, full moons, and the greater revolutions of the stars, exercise a great and manifest influence over natural bodies, it follows that the more exact and subtle positions of the stars must produce effects likewise more exquisite and secret. (DA 3iv, 350)

But Bacon pointed out that, besides the direct influences of the sun's heat and the moon's magnetism, there is no evidence for the planetary motions having any significant power over our lives and, this being so, one might argue with equal force that the slighter changes in the planets should have practically no effect on us at all. Thus, continuing the above remarks, Bacon argued that the astrologers

> ought first to have excepted the operations of the sun by manifest heat, and likewise the magnetic influence of the moon on the half-monthly tides . . . and then they will find the powers of the rest of the planets over natural things (as far as they are approved by experience) very weak and slight, and almost invisible, even in the greater revolutions. And therefore they should argue in a manner directly contrary; that as those greater revolutions have so little influence, these nice and minute differences of positions have no power at all. (DA 3iv, 350)

Bacon found this a persuasive argument and, in his proposals for a reformed or rational astrology *(astrologia sana)*, he made it a first rule to reject the doctrines of horoscopes and houses, which attribute effects to minute differences in planetary positions; however, he retained the idea that the greater revolutions of the planets make themselves felt on earth. As he put it: "The former are like great guns, and can strike from afar; the latter are like little bows, and cannot transmit their force over much space." (DA

3iv, 351) The other "rules" make the points that the heavenly bodies (excepting the effect of their heat) act only on the more "tender" kinds of body, "such as humours, air and spirit"; that different individuals are differently affected, some being "softer wax as it were"; and that, whatever influence the stars possess, they are such as "rather incline than compel" (DA 3iv, 351). It was a common objection to astrology that the stars cannot exert a fatal necessity over our lives, usually based on the doctrine of free-will and the theological notion that we are responsible for our deeds. The objection might more plausibly have been sustained on the grounds that the effects which come within the ambit of astrology are also partly the results of very many mundane influences. It is not clear on which, if either, of these arguments Bacon would have justified his view, for he stated it baldly.

Bacon had great hopes for a rational astrology formed upon these lines, for he held it "for certain that the celestial bodies have in them certain other influences besides heat and light" (DA 3iv, 351). Such an astrology would, first of all, gather information about the positions of the planets and stars relative to one another. It would also take account of anything concerning the nature and structure of the stars, as well as those "particular natures and inclinations of the planets, and likewise of the fixed stars, as handed down by tradition". Bacon maintained that these traditions "ought not (except when they are plainly at variance with physical reasons) to be lightly rejected." (DA 3iv, 353) An improved astrology would also survey the great commotions and disasters of the past and examine what the positions of the heavenly bodies were at the time. And, "where there is found a manifest agreement and coincidence of events, there a probable rule of prediction may be established." (DA 3iv, 355) This advice is irritatingly vague, but sensible so far as it goes. Bacon would, one assumes, have appreciated the kind of research carried out recently by Gauquelin, in which the times of birth of leading sportsmen and members of various professions were correlated with the positions of different planets. Gauquelin claims to have discovered remarkable coincidences of birth-time and planetary positions, which he took as evidence of a causal connexion. Bacon might well have approved the manner of investigation, though he would have been amazed by the claim that a planet could produce such significant effects in the brief periods it occupies its supposedly favourable positions.

5(iv) Alchemy

Bacon did not dismiss the established principles of alchemy for being unproven speculations, nor did he think that the aim of transmuting one substance into another was a vain one, an attitude which, incidentally, has been vindicated by modern developments in science. However, he rejected the particular means by which alchemists proposed to convert base metals into gold, and he believed it "a thing more probable" that a true understanding of the nature of weight, colour, etc. would enable this end to be reached (AL, 362). As I have already explained in Chapter Two, the main reason why Bacon disapproved of contemporary alchemy lay in what he judged to be the unscientific character of its methods, in which theories were adopted and retained while a mass of adverse evidence had been side-stepped by systematically inventing "frivolous", ad hoc hypotheses. Incidentally, Bacon arrived at this judgment at an early stage and his *Novum Organum* criticisms are repeated almost verbatim from his *Masculine Birth of Time* of 1603 (p. 74).

5(v) Astronomy

Bacon saw little of merit in the astronomy of his time and even Copernicus failed to impress him. It is often said that it was the fallible, hypothetical character of these sciences that repelled Bacon and that he preferred astronomers to avoid theories, at least until a solid basis of facts had been laid, on which they could be built with the assurance of a logical certainty. Thus Jardine (1974,

77) says that Bacon rejected the Copernican system in astronomy for being "merely a hypothesis consistent with the available data, and useful for making astronomical predictions, *but in no way guaranteed as true*" (my italics). R. F. Jones (1982, 52) summarised Bacon's attitude to astronomy and to the Copernican theory, in particular, in terms of "his injunction . . . to abjure theories and find out by observation and experiment what is actually in nature." Popper (1963, 264) referred to the "misplaced criticism . . . directed by Bacon against Copernicus" as an "ill-advised attempt to destroy metaphysics wholesale"; and Ellis, too, took Bacon to task for failing to realize that astronomy like any other science is bound to employ hypotheses. (1857b, 716–8)

It is no wonder that Bacon's disagreement with Copernicus has seemed to have arisen from the hypothetical, fallible character of the heliocentric theory, for Bacon certainly set himself against what he called the "hypotheses of astronomers", amongst which he classed the Copernican and Ptolemaic systems. Bacon charged such hypotheses with being unable to reveal "the truth of the thing" (DIG, 512) and, unlike "philosophy concerning celestial bodies", they would, he said, never lead to the "substance, motion, and influence of the heavenly bodies *as they really are.*" (DA 3iv, 348; my italics)

Such remarks do give the impression that Bacon was repelled by the speculativeness of the astronomical hypotheses of Copernicus and Ptolemy and was drawn to the certainty of "philosophy", and this would fit in well with the usual picture of him as an advocate of an infallible scientific method. However, there is good evidence that the distinction between "astronomical hypotheses" and a "philosophy concerning celestial bodies" did not mark out uncertain or fallible from certain and infallible science, but made the quite different division between physical theories and mere computational devices. This was a standard dichotomy of philosophical usage, which can be traced back at least to Plato, and was certainly employed in Bacon's time, by Gilbert, for instance. (1600, 318, 322, 343)

Simplicius, writing in the sixth century AD, explained the distinction between physical theories and astronomical hypotheses very clearly:

> To physical theory . . . belongs the study of all that concerns the essence of the heavens and the stars, their power, their quality, their generation and destruction. And, by Zeus, physics also has the power of providing demonstrations concerning the size, shape, and arrangement of these bodies. Astronomy, on the other hand, is not prepared to say anything about the former. . . . The astronomer is not equipped to contemplate causes . . . [and] feels obliged to posit certain hypothetical modes of being which are such that, once conceded, the phenomena are saved. (quoted in Duhem, 1908, 10–11)

Osiander wrote, in a similar vein, to Copernicus, saying that he had "always felt about hypotheses that they are not articles of faith but the basis of computation", their role being to "reproduce exactly the phenomena of the motions" (quoted in Rosen, 1939, 22). And, in his preface to Copernicus' *De Revolutionibus,* he said of astronomical hypotheses that they "need not be true nor even probable; if they provide a calculus consistent with the observations, that alone is sufficient", adding that when "there are offered for one and the same motion different hypotheses (as eccentricity and an epicycle for the sun's motion), the astronomer will accept above all others the one which is the easiest to grasp." By contrast: "The philosopher will perhaps rather seek the semblance of the truth." (quoted in Rosen, 1939, 25)

Thus the theories of philosophy are concerned with those material properties of the heavens which constitute the physical causes of celestial phenomena. Astronomy, on the other hand, advances hypotheses which are not intended to describe those causes, but represent ways of arranging directly observable phenomena, such as the relative positions and velocities of the heavenly bodies. When one astronomer proposes to explain the sun's motion with an eccentric, while another employs an epicycle, there is no disagreement regarding the physical nature of things, provided that both save the phenomena equally well, though one may perhaps be preferred on aesthetic grounds or for reasons of simplicity. Bacon was clearly employing this traditional characterisation when referring to the hypotheses of astronomy:

> it is useless to refute them, because they are not themselves asserted as true, and they may be various and contrary one to the other, yet so as equally to save and adjust the phenomena. (TH, 557)

> Neither indeed do they [Copernicus, Ptolemy, and Tycho Brahe] who propose these theories mean to say that the things they allege are actually true, but only that they are *convenient hypotheses for calculations and the construction of tables.* (DIG, 511; my italics)

> astronomy presents only the exterior of the heavenly bodies (I mean the number of the stars, their positions, motions, and periods), as it were the hide of the heavens; beautiful indeed and skilfully arranged into systems; but the interior (namely the physical reasons) is wanting, out of which (with the help of astronomical hypotheses) a theory might be devised which would not merely satisfy the phenomena (of which kind many might with a little ingenuity be contrived), but which would set forth the substance, motion, and influence of the heavenly bodies as they really are. (DA 3iv, 348)

Bacon's reservations about the hypotheses of astronomy were clearly, then, unconnected with any merely speculative character they might have possessed. Quite the reverse. Astronomy's weakness, in Bacon's estimation, lay in the failure of its hypotheses to deal with the inner natures of the heavens, which, while not immediately perceptible, contain the real physical causes of celestial phenomena. The hypotheses of astronomy have some of the characteristic failings of those axioms which Bacon referred to as anticipations of nature: they do not penetrate to the deeper recesses of nature but stick to its surface phenomena; and, it will be recalled, such axioms are also regularly "rescued and preserved by some frivolous distinction" when they lead to false predictions. This kind of rescue service was always on hand in astronomy, where every anomaly could be resolved by "that multiplication of circles complicated at pleasure" (TH, 556).

Rather than seeking to preserve the fiction of circular motion by the ever more cumbrous machinery of eccentrics and epicycles, it would be better, Bacon believed, if astronomers were to give up that idea and try other curves. Bacon pointed out, quite rightly, that the planets move in spirals, and he argued that the precise shapes of these should be described. (TH, 553) We cannot be sure how he would have reacted to Kepler's approximately true law of elliptical motion. (Although Kepler published his first law of elliptical motion in 1609, Bacon seems to have been unaware of this and to have known practically nothing of Kepler and his writings.)

The philosophy that Bacon hoped would supersede the work hitherto attempted would inquire into the "physical causes" of planetary motions and these, he believed, were to be sought in "the most universal appetites and passions of matter" (DA 3iv, 349):

> the truth is that, without meaning to throw away the benefit of former inventions, I am attempting a far greater work: for it is not merely calculations or predictions that I aim at, but philosophy: such a philosophy I mean as may inform the human understanding, not only of the motion of the heavenly bodies and the period of that motion, but likewise of their substance, various qualities, powers, and influences . . . (DIG, 511)

Bacon was operating here with the principle that changes are always brought about by other physical bodies ("for bodies are not acted on except by bodies"; NO II, xxxv), and never by a mere position or "mathematical point" which, if it did exert an influence, "would be a wonderful and efficacious sort of nothing" (NO II, xxxv). Bacon concluded:

the best hope and security for the study of celestial bodies I place in physical reasons; meaning by physical reasons not such as are commonly supposed, but only the doctrine concerning those appetites of matter which no diversity of regions or places can distract or dissever. (DIG, 512)

It seems probable that Bacon would have been delighted with the Newtonian revolution which, insofar as it was based on the idea of universal gravitation, carried his recommendations into effect. But he would, presumably, have been less sympathetic to the supposed causal efficacy which absolute space enjoys in Newton's system.

Despite the severity of Bacon's criticisms, he did not wish to say that astronomy was entirely useless; its hypotheses have some value "for compendious calculation" (TH, 557) and it "has indeed a good foundation in phenomena" (DA 3iv, 347). Astronomical hypotheses posed a danger to philosophy, however, when the caveats of astronomers as to the purely instrumental or conventional significance of their theories were ignored and they received a realistic interpretation. For, as substantive accounts of the physical nature of the heavens, both the Ptolemaic and Copernican theories had to be rejected as false. They both relied, so Bacon argued, on the erroneous principle of an incorruptible superlunary substance composing the heavens. This in turn led to the idea of the *primum mobile* in the Ptolemaic system, and to the diurnal motion of the earth, in the Copernican system.

Bacon rejected the Aristotelian distinction between matter above and matter below the moon, on rational grounds, reasoning that "between heaven and earth, as regards constancy and change, there is not much difference" (DIG, 526). First of all, Bacon pointed out that the heavens are not altogether immutable, in view of reports of new and disappeared stars, and of dramatic changes in the appearance of the sun and of some of the planets. Moreover, the heavens are so immense that, even if large changes in them did take place, we might not be able to detect them, just as an earthquake would be invisible from the moon. (DIG, 527) And then, as we only see a relatively small portion of the earth, there is no reason to think that it is, overall, subject to so very much alteration.

Bacon also expressed himself against the idea that the earth has a diurnal motion, as postulated by the Copernicans. He said he was "convinced [it] is most false" (DA 3iv, 348).

Bacon's rejection of Copernicanism has struck many observers as resulting from an imperious and unreasoned bias, all the more regrettable and hypocritical considering what he had to say against those who allowed blind prejudice to dictate their views. Hume, for instance, in his *History of England* (Appendix to the reign of James I), reported him as having rejected the Copernican system "with the most positive disdain", Quinton (1980) also mentions disdain in this context, and Popper has written that he "sneered at those who denied the self-evident truth that the sun and the stars rotated round the earth, which was obviously at rest" (1962, II, 16). As so often in his discussion of Bacon, Popper seems to distance himself as far as possible from the truth. For Bacon never sneered at the heliocentric theory, nor did he come to, or advance, his opinion in the high-handed and intemperate manner which is insinuated. In fact, as Whewell (1857, 295–7) observed, Bacon examined the question of the earth's motion carefully, he judged it empirically and concluded tentatively.

It seems probable that Bacon was against the doctrine from at least 1592, when he referred, with seeming sarcasm, to "these new carmen which drive the earth about" *(In Praise of Knowledge)*. Then, is his *Valerius Terminus*, he observed that, though "astronomy itself cannot correct" the Copernican thesis because it is compatible with the phenomena, "yet natural philosophy doth correct [it]" (VT, 229). In a somewhat later work he looked to information about the "universal passions of matter" to settle the question: "For he who knows [these] . . . thereby knows what is possible to be" (DIG, 512). Bacon declared himself more definitely opposed to the doctrine in the *Theory of the Heaven* (p. 551), written around 1612, where he thought it "the truer opinion" that the earth is stationary. However, his opinion was cautious and tentative. Referring to his denial that the earth revolves and to a number of other cosmological speculations, he concluded cautiously, "I do not mean to bind myself to these [opinions]; for in them as in other things I am certain of my way, but not certain of my position" (TH, 559). Bacon's opposition to the diurnal motion of the earth seems to have hardened somewhat by the time he translated the *Advancement of Learning*, now finding himself "convinced [that it] is most false" (DA 3iv, 348). On the other hand, he does not seem to have thought the evidence yet existed that would entirely vindicate this opinion, for he now said (translating and slightly moderating corresponding remarks in the *Valerius Terminus*) that, though the earth's diurnal motion cannot be refuted by astronomical principles, "yet the principles of natural philosophy *rightly laid down may* correct it" (DA 4i, 373; my italics). Finally, in the *Novum Organum*, he objected to Galileo's theory of the tides, saying that it is "devised upon an assumption which cannot be granted *(concesso non concessibili)*, viz. that the earth moves" (NO II, xlvi).

Spedding translated the Latin phrase above as "cannot be allowed", which leaves it ambiguous as to whether Bacon would not *permit* the assumption, because he was convinced it was false, or whether he would not *concede* it, because it was uncertain, whereas the second seems to be the intended meaning. For an assumption which cannot be granted as the foundation and presupposition of a theory of the tides is not one that necessarily must be rejected as definitely false. It may simply lack the degree of security which it would need in order to provide any substantial justification for another theory. It is not unreasonable to say that this was just the position that the hypothesis of the earth's diurnal motion held at the beginning of the seventeenth century. (It is worth mentioning in passing that Bacon's other and very cogent objection to Galileo's theory was that it predicted two tides a day when in fact there were four. (NO II, xlvi))

Bacon did not state directly the reasons why he believed the earth was stationary, but they are easily gathered from different parts of his writings. In the *Novum Organum*, he described a crucial experiment which was to determine "whether the Diurnal

Motion, whereby to our eyes the sun and stars rise and set, be a
real motion of rotation in the heavenly bodies, or a motion
apparent in the heavenly bodies, and real in the earth." The
experiment sought to establish whether the east-west motion of
the heavenly bodies and of things near the earth, but not attached
to it, was "most rapid in the highest parts of the heavens, and
gradually falling off, and finally stopping and becoming extinct in
the immoveable—that is, the earth" (NO II, xxxvi). Bacon
described the observations which would suffice to decide this
point:

> If there be found in the ocean any motion from east to
> west, however weak and languid; if the same motion be
> found a little quicker in the air, especially within the tropics,
> where because of the larger circles it is more perceptible;
> if the same motion be found in the lower comets, but
> now lively and vigorous; if the same motion be found in
> planets, but so distributed and graduated, that the nearer
> a planet is to the earth its motion is slower, the further a
> planet is distant from the earth its motion is quicker, and
> quickest of all in the starry sphere; then indeed we should
> receive the diurnal motion as real in the heavens, and deny
> such motion to the earth; because it will be manifest that
> motion from east to west is perfectly cosmical, and by
> consent of the universe . . . (NO II, xxxvi)

The *Novum Organum* presents this experiment merely as a
proposal, but Bacon clearly felt confident its result would favour a
stationary earth. Even his earliest brief foray against the
astronomers took it to be obvious that, contrary to their opinion,
"the nearer [bodies are to] the earth the slower" *(In Praise of
Knowledge).* This view is expressed again in the *Theory of the
Heaven,* and in his work *On the Ebb and Flow of the Sea.*
Although devoted primarly to investigating the causes and nature
of tidal motion, the latter work was also "connected with the
inquiry whether the earth has a diurnal motion" (*Works* V, 458)
and contains a detailed survey of celestial phenomena. The
empirical arguments against the diurnal motion, apart from the

hopeless unreliability of the data themselves, are not very powerful ones and Bacon was mistaken in thinking that they discriminate between a rotating earth and a rotating heaven, for both could produce the same results. But, though guilty of this error, he was innocent of what, for a philosopher of science, would be the greater sin of peremptorily dismissing the Copernican theory. And I, for one, would be reluctant to condemn Bacon's conclusion as demonstrating "his lack of scientific judgement", as Horton (1973, 273) has done, until I had seen better reasons than have so far been published for why an early seventeenth century philosopher should have preferred the Copernican system over Ptolemy's. Incidentally, Tycho Brahe (1546–1601), who was not a negligible astronomer, also held that the earth was stationary and Bacon regarded his efforts to combine this point of view with the advantages of Copernicanism as very promising. (DIG, 511)

5(vi) Mathematics

Bacon held no very remarkable or original views on the nature and role of mathematics and the main reason that we need to deal with them at some length is to answer those who have attributed to him bizarre or wrongheaded opinions. Bacon seems to have acquired a reputation for undervaluing the contribution that mathematics can make to natural science at a very early stage. For instance, Seth Ward, the man who proposed Newton for membership of the Royal Society, observed in 1654 that "it was a misfortune to the world that my Lord Bacon was not skilled in mathematics and this made him jealous of their assistance in natural inquiries." (1654, 25) The idea that Bacon granted little or nothing to mathematics in the process of induction has made its way down to the present day and has contributed to the interpretation of his philosophy by many of his leading expositors. Recently, for instance, Anthony Quinton (1980, 47) remarked that:

> It has long been a familiar, and well-founded, criticism of Bacon's philosophy of science that it does not adequately

> recognise the role in science of mathematics . . . he does not
> recognise the *indispensable* place of mathematics in science.

And Dijksterhuis counted his "undervaluation of mathematics" as
one of Bacon's defects, than which "nothing is easier to enlarge
on" (1961, 402). Thorndike, similarly, held his "total disregard of
mathematical method" to be his greatest defect (1958, 67).

Two explanations have been offered for Bacon's commonly
supposed inability to "see the indispensable necessity of
mathematics in the great *Instauration* which he projected"
(Church, 1909, 195). The first is expressed in Seth Ward's remark,
namely that Bacon's lack of proficiency in mathematics made him
blind to, or prejudiced against, what it can achieve in physics. It
is certainly true that Bacon was neither a skilled nor a very
knowledgeable mathematician, but I shall, in due course, dispute
the claim that this produced in him a jealous or dismissive
attitude to mathematics or to its role in science.

The second reason why Bacon is supposed to have discounted
any great significance for mathematics in physical science derives
from a general view of his method as aiming merely at correlating
simple, qualitative natures. As Jardine puts it, "the first principles
envisaged by Bacon for science . . . are to be definitions in terms
of essential qualities of natural phenomena". And this, says Jardine
(1973, 78), "automatically means that mathematics plays only a
subsidiary rôle in Baconian science", for "Number and quality
are, in the Aristotelian scheme, accidental, not essential attributes
of bodies." Since Jardine regards Bacon as, in this respect, within
the Aristotelian scheme, her conclusion follows. Quite what a
"subsidiary rôle" entails is not altogether clear, however, though
Jardine tries to illustrate the idea with the claim that "Bacon
believed that it was extremely misguided to search for laws of
proportionality in nature". If Bacon had really taken such a stand
against particular types of mathematico-physical theories, it would
indeed have revealed a lamentable prejudice. But it seems to me
that he did not, and the remarks of Bacon's on which Jardine seeks
to rest her case cannot reasonably be taken as supporting it.
Bacon's complaint in that quotation was that

men believe that if the quantity be increased or multiplied,
the power and virtue is increased or multiplied
proportionately. And this they postulate and suppose *as if it
had a kind of mathematical certainty; which is utterly false.*
(DA 5ii, 414; my italics)

Bacon then gave some simple and unexceptionable examples to
demonstrate this falsity, the most charming concerning the
woman in Aesop's fable "who expected that with a double measure
of barley her hen would lay two eggs a day; whereas the hen grew
fat and laid none". Bacon's remarks certainly do not imply a wish
to dismiss laws of proportionality wholesale; he was just issuing a
reasonable warning, in keeping with the rest of his anti-dogmatic
philosophy, against the tendency, which he thought he had
detected, automatically to assume laws of proportionality, without
carefully checking these by varying the conditions of an
experiment.

Consider now what Bacon said about mathematics. He
followed the tradition of dividing mathematics into "pure" and
"mixed" (i.e., applied) branches. The former handles "Quantity
Determinate, merely severed from any axioms of natural
philosophy", and comprises geometry and arithmetic; the latter
"hath for subject some axioms or parts of natural philosophy, and
considereth Quantity determined, as it is auxiliary and incident
unto them." (AL, 360) In other words, mixed mathematics
employs physical laws cast in mathematical form, in order to
describe the quantitative aspects of nature. Bacon had no
substantial complaint against pure mathematics, though he
regretted that it had developed little since ancient times (DA 3vi,
370–1). He also remarked, en passant, that the value of pure
mathematics in training the mind had not received the attention it
deserved:

In the Mathematics I can report no deficience, except it be
that men do not sufficiently understand the excellent use of
the Pure Mathematics, in that they do remedy and cure
many defects in the wit and faculties intellectual. For if the
wit be too dull, they sharpen it; if too wandering, they fix it;

> if too inherent in the sense, they abstract it. So that as tennis
> is a game of no use in itself, but of great use in respect it
> maketh a quick eye and a body ready to put itself into all
> postures; so in the Mathematics, that use which is collateral
> and intervenient is no less worthy than that which is
> principal and intended. (AL, 360)

These last words have been grievously misunderstood by several authors, to the detriment of Bacon's reputation. Thorndike, for example, reported that: "He spoke of mathematics as, like the game of tennis, of no use in itself but as good exercise to cure intellectual defects" (1958, 67)." And Hochberg: "For Francis Bacon, induction was the sole method of empirical science. Mathematics he hardly mentions, and, when he does, he seems to believe that its chief utility is the sharpening of 'wits'" (1953, 322).

But Bacon obviously did not mean that mathematics had a value *only* or even mainly as mental gymnastics, for he was merely pointing out, what is surely true, that besides its primary merit as a branch of learning, its study can produce the admirable effect of improving the powers of reasoning. Descartes made much the same point a few years later in his *Rules for the Direction of the Mind.*

There is a great deal of evidence that mathematics, particularly mixed mathematics, occupied a very important place in Bacon's conception of science. Consider, for instance, the following:

> many parts of nature can neither be invented with sufficient
> subtilty nor demonstrated with sufficient perspicuity nor
> accommodated unto use with sufficient dexterity, without the
> aid and intervening of the Mathematics . . . (AL, 360).

The subjects he mentioned in this context were "Perspective, Music, Astronomy, Cosmography, Architecture, Enginery and divers others." Bacon's prediction concerning mixed mathematics was "that there cannot fail to be more kinds of them, as nature grows further disclosed." (AL, 361)

As his thoughts developed, Bacon seems only to have become more decided on the importance of mathematics in science, as the discussion it received in his *De Augmentis* shows. There, he reaffirmed the vital role he had envisaged for mixed mathematics, and renewed his prediction that

> as Physic advances farther and farther every day and
> develops new axioms, it will require fresh assistance from
> Mathematic in many things, and so the parts of Mixed
> Mathematics will be more numerous. (DA 3vi, 371)

Bacon also gave a reason why this discipline should occupy so central a position. It was that mathematics describes quantity, which is an important causal agent in the physical world:

> For Quantity (which is the subject of Mathematic), when
> applied to matter, is as it were the dose of Nature, and is the
> cause of a number of effects in things natural; and therefore it
> must be reckoned as one of the Essential Forms of things.
> (DA 3iv, 369–70)

Bacon's words hardly indicate a desire to relegate mathematics to a lowly station and they flatly contradict those, such as Quinton, who accuse him of having "no real sense" of the fact that natural science was, even in his own time, a largely quantitative study (1980, 47). Bacon was clearly very much aware of this.

Bacon also placed great weight on experiments and observations of a quantitative nature and he judged the "chief cause of failure" to produce new works to be "the ill determination and measurement of the forces and actions of bodies." (NO II, xliv) With this in mind, Bacon described four kinds of quantitative observation, which he held to be important for many areas of study. A measure of the significance these "mathematical instances" held in Bacon's scheme is that they occupy nearly a third of the space devoted to the various types of observation— the so-called prerogative instances—which he regarded as being particularly valuable in scientific induction. I shall discuss the mathematical instances here, and deal with the other prerogative instances in the next chapter.

The first of the mathematical instances (instances of the Rod) concern the motions of bodies and the forces acting between them: "For the powers and motions of things act and take effect at distances, not indefinite or accidental, but finite and fixed; so that to ascertain and observe these distances in the investigation of the several natures is of the greatest advantage to practice" (NO II, xlv). He mentioned a number of phenomena which "should be observed and brought to computation": the way magnetic and electric forces vary with distance, mass, etc.; the variations of visual acuity under different circumstances; the degree to which different bodies are susceptible to expansion and compression, and so on. Bacon even described some modest experiments of his own, in which he had investigated the different extents to which air and water can be compressed. "All these things with their measures should in the investigation of nature be explored and set down, either in their certitude, or by estimate, or by comparison, as the case will admit." (NO II, xlv) Other mathematical instances (instances of the Course) concern variations of natural processes with time, such as the periods of revolution of the heavenly bodies; the manner in which the powers of bodies vary with the quantity of matter within them (instances of Quantity); and, lastly, the comparative strengths of different powers or virtues (instances of Strife). Bacon held it to be of the greatest importance to make careful measurements of all these things, devoting a good deal of space and employing many detailed examples to illustrate his ideas.

It is significant, too, that one of the few theories describing the form of a nature which Bacon himself advanced, while it may be no gem from the treasury of science, nevertheless is of a quantitative form. I refer to his explanation of colour, which he located in the smaller parts of bodies, particular colours being produced when the sizes of these are in corresponding proportions. The few experiments that Bacon said he himself performed were also mainly quantitative, most notably his experiments to measure the relative densities of different substances. These were carefully conducted by comparing the weights of two identical prisms, one empty and the other filled, and they issued in precise results for seventy–eight different materials. (*The History of Dense and Rare; Works* V, 339–48)

It is remarkable, after all this, that Bacon is so frequently reckoned to have lacked a proper appreciation of the role and significance of mathematics in science. We must, however, consider how his reputation as an undervaluer of mathematics arose. The responsibility seems to lie in some brief remarks that appeared for the first time in his later work, the *De Augmentis*, where he said that mathematics "ought rather to be placed among Appendices than among Substantive Sciences" (DA 3vi, 369) and that both mathematics and logic should be "but the handmaids of Physic" (DA 3vi, 370).

Whether Bacon warrants his reputation on the basis of these qualifications, is, I think, highly doubtful; it seems to me, on the contrary, that they show a very lively appreciation of the proper part for mathematics within science. The reasoning behind Bacon's qualifications was this. He was a great classifier and therefore wished to find a suitable slot for mathematics in his taxonomy of knowledge. Aristotle had assigned it to a separate division from physics and metaphysics, on account of its supposedly separate subject matter. Bacon disagreed with this and thought that, if mathematics were to be set down as "a substantive and principal science", then it would be "more agreeable both to the nature of the thing and the clearness of order to place it as a branch of Metaphysic", his reason for this having already been noted, namely that "Quantity . . . is the cause of a number of effects in things natural; and therefore it must be reckoned as one of the Essential Forms of things" (DA 3iv, 369–70). However, it has also to be acknowledged that "of all natural forms . . . Quantity is the most abstracted and separable from matter" (DA 3iv, 370), and so can be applied to various fields. This seems to be the reason why he said:

> I have thought it better to designate Mathematics, seeing that they are of so much importance both in Physics and Metaphysics and Mechanics and Magic, as appendices and auxiliaries to them all. (DA 3iv, 370)

This seems both to upgrade and to demote mathematics, for on the one hand it reserves an honoured place for the subject, not just in metaphysics, but in physics and in the application of these two branches of knowledge to practice, mechanics being the applied or operative part of physics, and magic of metaphysics.

On the other hand, mathematics is restricted to the "appendices and auxiliaries" of these sciences. Bacon felt compelled, he said, to make this estimate, because of "the daintiness and pride of mathematicians, who will needs have this science almost domineer over Physic". For Bacon had observed that

> it has come to pass, I know not how, that Mathematic and Logic, which ought to be but the handmaids of Physic, nevertheless presume *on the strength of the certainty which they possess* to exercise dominion over it. But the place and dignity of this science is of less importance . . . (DA 3iv, 370; my italics).

Unfortunately, Bacon did not go into details about this complaint against the mathematicians, but it is not unreasonable to infer that he objected to their influence in areas such as astronomy, which "as it now is, is fairly enough ranked among the mathematical arts" (DA 3iv, 349). He also referred to "that piece of mathematical elegance, the reduction of motions to perfect circles" (TH, 551) and to "the mathematicians [who] cannot satisfy themselves, except they reduce the motions of the celestial bodies to perfect circles" (AL, 395). Astronomy was traditionally called 'mathematical', and the term 'mathematical hypotheses', as a synonym for hypotheses which are "*nothing but* instruments for the prediction of appearances", is preserved even in modern usage. (Popper, 1963, 173)

As Bacon had previously explained, the principal defect of such investigations, when they are handled mathematically, is that the inner physical causes are missed, for their prime concern is merely to devise a framework for encapsulating the data economically. But he held that such frameworks were not entirely useless, as the facts they comprehend may form a valuable foundation for a more penetrating science, which will look into the underlying physical causes of the phenomena. Bacon made a similar point in regard to investigations of light, which, he regretted, had been treated hitherto only as a geometric phenomenon rather than with a view to revealing its physical nature. Hesse (1964, 147) summarised Bacon's view thus: "Bacon would be satisfied with a wave or corpuscular theory of light, but not with mere geometric optics." One could argue, in defence of the mathematical approach, that the discovery of a particular mathematical structure of the phenomena might well suggest, and give evidence of, some corresponding physical basis, for instance as in the case of the laws of reflection of light and those governing the rebounding of elastic spheres from smooth surfaces. Bacon should have been receptive to this defence, for he appreciated the fact that such analogies are "very serviceable in revealing the fabric of the parts of the universe" (NO II, xxvii).

Bacon's relegation of logic to belowstairs is no more unscientific than his similar treatment of mathematics and certainly cannot be taken as excluding the usual logical operations from science. The logic that he ruled out of bounds was a specific kind of presumptuous reasoning, which he connected with Aristotle and his followers. Logic, he correctly observed, "ought to enter the several provinces of science armed with a higher authority than belongs to the principles of those sciences themselves, and ought to call those putative principles to account until they are fully established" (*Plan*, 25–6). But the logicians Bacon had in mind "borrow the principles of each science from the science itself"; they "hold in reverence the first notions of the mind", and "receive as conclusive the immediate informations of the sense, when well disposed" (*Plan*, 25). Bacon opposed these tendencies as part of his case against anticipating nature, but his opposition is no signal that he intended to banish logic, in the present-day sense of the word, from physics, or that he wished it demoted beneath its proper place.

One might perhaps have welcomed a more detailed exposition by Bacon of his opinions, but there seems no reason at all to censure him for their content; his idea of the status that mathematics should occupy in science seems exactly right, if less exciting than the view often attributed to him. As he said, the quantitative aspect of nature means that mathematics is vitally important in formulating the fundamental axioms of science. But this should not mean that science becomes a kind of mathematics, such as arithmetic or algebra, for these are a priori disciplines, not themselves descriptive of the world, except in the most abstract sense. Mathematics is a subject which "ought only to give definiteness to natural philosophy, not to generate or give it birth" (NO I, xcvi). Thus, it seems entirely reasonable and correct to say of mathematics, and similarly of logic, that they play their parts in physical science as essential auxiliaries and "handmaids".

5(vii) Biology

Harvey.   Bacon is often criticized for ignoring William Harvey's great discoveries concerning the circulation of the blood, perhaps out of jealousy or from an ignorant failure to appreciate their value. Harvey (1578–1657), who is reputed to have been his physician, evidently entertained a low opinion of Bacon the philosopher, though our only information on this derives from Harvey's putative remark that Bacon "writes philosophy like a Lord Chancellor". This presumably uncomplimentary jibe was retailed by the unreliable and frequently inebriate Aubrey twenty-three years after Harvey's death and fifty years after Bacon's, and on that account, as Hale-White observed (1927, 32), should perhaps not be taken too seriously.

Harvey's work was passed over in Bacon's review of the science of his day, but I think we should not judge ill of Bacon on that account. The most probable explanation for the omission is that he either had never heard of Harvey's theory, or else lacked the opportunity to assess the evidence in its favour. For Harvey did not actually publish his findings until after Bacon's death, his exposition of them before that, from 1616 on, being confined to lectures at the Royal College of Physicians.

Even if Bacon had attended Harvey's lectures, we do not know how persuasive he ought to have found the evidence then available, since Harvey himself related that his book was issued only after more than nine years, during which, as he said in the dedication to his *De Motu Cordis* (p. 5), he had "confirmed these views by multiplied demonstrations . . . , illustrated them by arguments, and freed them from the objections of the most learned and skilful anatomists". However, it is unlikely that Bacon would have had leisure enough to attend Harvey's lectures, for in 1616 he was approaching the summit of his career and was an extremely busy public servant. No doubt he would have had more time after his impeachment, but by then he was in poor health, and burdened by debt. All in all, then, Bacon probably knew little if anything of Harvey's discoveries, and so we have no reason to think he tried to suppress them, and no grounds to blame him for ignoring them.

Medicine.   Bacon was unhappy about the state of medical science as it was practised by his contemporaries, though he conceded that it was attended by special difficulties. In particular, he believed its subject matter, the human body, to be extremely complex, as it lies at the end of a long biological chain; for the rain nourishes plants, which are then consumed by animals, these in turn being eaten by men. Added to this, we have a much more varied manner of life than beasts. (DA 4ii, 380)

On account of this complexity, the medical "art (especially as we now have it) must be reckoned as one of the most conjectural", a fact which has "made so much more room not only for error, but also for imposture" (DA 4ii, 379 and 380). One of the difficulties in judging medical practitioners is that one has nothing to go on but whether the patient recovers or not after treatment. Much the same is true of politicians. But "who can know, if a patient die or recover, or if a state be preserved or ruined, whether it be art or accident?" It is, therefore, not surprising that "many times the impostor is prized, and the man of virtue censured." (DA 4ii, 381) The case is different with a lawyer and with the master of a ship, who need not be judged by "the issue of the cause" or by "the fortune of the voyage", but can display their abilities directly, with the power of their pleading and their skill in steering. (DA 4ii, 380–1) Hence Bacon's apophthegm concerning a painter turned physician to whom it was said: "You have done well; for before the faults of your work were seen, but now they are unseen." (*Works* VII, 160–1)

The fundamental problem lies in the state of the medical art, which Bacon suggested is not built on a solid empirical foundation but on two sorts of useless generalities. The first of these consists of theories which, "though true, have the fault that they do not well lead the way to action"; the second contains more pernicious generalities, "which are in themselves false, and instead of leading mislead" (DA 4ii, 383).

Bacon divided the task of medicine three ways: into the preservation of health, the cure of diseases and the prolongation of life. (DA 4ii, 383) In regard to the first, he suggested that diet, particularly respecting the quantities ingested, should be the subject of investigation and that more emphasis ought to be placed on physical exertion, since "there is scarcely any tendency to disease which may not be prevented by some proper exercise" (DA 4ii, 384). He listed bowls, archery, walking, and riding as being especially beneficial; had he known of them, it is unlikely that he would have included either squash or jogging, as he thought that "exercise that is too rapid and violent, as running, games at ball, fencing, and the like, are injurious" (*The History of Life and Death, Works* V, 278). Unfortunately, Bacon did not disclose the source of his wisdom on these matters.

The cure of diseases would be promoted, he thought, if physicians returned to the "very useful and accurate diligence of Hippocrates, who used to set down a narrative of the special cases of his patients; relating what was the nature of the disease, what the treatment, and what the issue", as for instance was standardly done by lawyers "who have ever been careful to report the more important cases and new decisions, for instruction and direction in future cases" (DA 4ii, 384). Bacon also encouraged careful anatomical studies, for just as people differ markedly in their outward appearance, so too do their internal organs vary: "And in these very differences . . . are often found the 'causes continent' of many diseases" (DA 4ii, 385).

Human vivisection also is necessary if certain types of information are to be found out and, although "hateful and inhuman" (DA 4ii, 386), it may sometimes be justified by the compensating utility of the knowledge gained. He had no such reservations about animal vivisection and would not have protested at the revolting experiments that Harvey was then using to prove his ideas; however, he did say that "a little judgment" is required before a knowledge of animal anatomy can be transferred to human subjects. (DA 4ii, 386)

A serious threat to the advancement of medical learning comes from those craven souls who, without even making any physical inquiry, imperiously pronounce a disease incurable and thereby "enact a law of neglect, and exempt ignorance from discredit" (AL, 375); they thus make quite sure that no progress can be made.

Physicians should also consider it their task to mitigate the pains of disease, not just when this conduces to recovery "but also when, all hope of recovery being gone, it serves only to make a fair and easy passage from life" (DA 4ii, 387). Bacon was an early advocate of euthanasia:

> in our times, the physicians make a kind of scruple and
> religion to stay with the patient after he is given up; whereas
> in my judgment, if they would not be wanting to their office,
> and indeed to humanity, they ought both to acquire the skill
> and to bestow the attention whereby the dying may pass
> more easily and quietly out of life. (DA 4ii, 387)

The third branch of medical science, the prolongation of life, was a subject then much under discussion, in particular by

alchemists. It inspired Bacon to undertake an extensive
investigation, which he issued in 1623, under the title *The History
of Life and Death*. This work contains a huge collection of
observations concerning the ways that various objects are
preserved, and reports of remarkable cases of longevity and of
substances which affect the "spirits". Here are a few examples:

> The Irish, especially the wild Irish, are, even to this day,
> very long-lived. In truth, they say that within these few years
> the Countess of Desmond lived to 140, and shed her teeth
> three times. Now the Irish have a custom of standing naked
> before the fire, and rubbing and as it were pickling
> themselves with old salt butter. (*Works* V, 285)

> I knew also a nobleman, who lived to a great age, who every
> morning, directly he awoke, had a clod of fresh earth placed
> beneath his nose for him to smell. (*Works* V, 275) [This
> eccentric behaviour was evidently intended to have a calming
> effect, supplying "a good coolness to the spirits".]

> Land is most enriched by nitrous bodies; for all manure is
> nitrous, which is a sign of the spirit in nitre [the main
> ingredient of gunpowder]. (*Works* V, 274)

> The Turks use . . . a kind of herb, called "coffee," which they
> dry, grind to powder, and drink in warm water. They affirm
> that it gives no small vigour both to their courage and their
> wit. Yet this taken in large quantities will excite and disturb
> the mind; which shows it to be of a similar nature to opiates.
> (*Works* V, 271)

Bacon drew a variety of vague and "provisional rules" from this
odd assortment of facts (and alleged facts), such as that "In every
tangible body there is a spirit covered and enveloped in the
grosser body; and from this spirit consumption and dissolution
take their origin" (*Works* V, 321).

I think it not unfair to judge Bacon's contribution to medical
knowledge as slight. Nevertheless, many of his critical remarks on
the methodology of medicine were exceptional for the age, they
were well observed, and some of his suggestions were valuable.

5(viii) Summary

The unflattering picture which Russell painted of Bacon's competence to judge what is meritorious in science is, I think, not borne out by a closer analysis. Bacon did not reject Harvey's theory concerning the circulation of the blood, and his failure to report on it probably indicates that he, not surprisingly, knew little or nothing about Harvey's discoveries. His qualified praise for Gilbert was rightly qualified if, as seems likely, he was rejecting the alleged magnetic basis of the diurnal motion of the earth. The criticisms of the other sciences were reasoned and undogmatic, interesting and largely correct. Their interest lies particularly in the illustration they give of the poor method of anticipation, an illustration which, moreover, corroborates the present reading of that method. For Bacon did not accuse the various sciences of being speculative or fallible, as we should expect on the basis of what I earlier called the standard reading of the notion of anticipation. On the contrary, the faults he found were just those that I have argued were the characteristic faults of anticipations—astronomy failed to inquire into physical causes and concentrated merely upon categorising surface phenomena. Moreover, astronomical theories were fixed and protected by defence mechanisms which were applied systematically, irrespective of the plausibility of the resulting theories and without regard to whether they led to new predictions. Alchemists also sought an illusory security for their principles by these means, as did astrologers, who compounded these errors by actually ignoring adverse evidence. Mathematics is a crucial tool in science, for many of the best physical theories are bound to be precise and quantitative; but, as Bacon rightly pointed out, science abandons its proper reliance on experiment and observation if it becomes a part of mathematics, as astronomy had done, and as some critics, I believe, have alleged of certain branches of modern economics.

Chapter Six
The Role of Experiment

The eye of the understanding is like the eye of the sense; for as you may see great objects through small crannies or levels, so you may see great axioms of nature through small and contemptible instances.
(Sylva, 377).

6(i) Introduction

Bacon is famous for having championed experiment and observation, against authority and tradition, as sources of knowledge. Although not new in its general outline, the extent and detail of his arguments in favour of an experimental method put him well ahead of most rivals for the attention and respect of those concerned with scientific method in the seventeenth century. His writings were very widely circulated, the *Sylva Sylvarum*, which (apart from the *Essays*) seems to have been the most popular, going through at least twenty editions in the period from 1626 to 1685. (See Gibson, 1950.) His ideas were clearly part of the inspiration for the Royal Society. Thomas Sprat, the official historian of that society, thought that the best preface to his

History would be some of Bacon's writings, for he regarded Bacon's arguments as "the best . . . that can be produc'd for the defence of Experimental Philosophy; and the best directions, that are needful to promote it". (Sprat, 1667, 35–6) And a multitude of empirical studies carried out in the years after his death bear the stamp of Bacon's authority and example, and also of his terminology. To take one instance, Boyle (1661, 13–14) presented certain experimental results as "Particulars [which] . . . were in my first Designe collected in order to [be] a Continuation of the Lord *Verulam's Sylva Sylvarum,* or Natural History."

But despite the high regard in which his ideas on experimental science were held by his near contemporaries (some of them, like Boyle and Hooke, very good scientists), Bacon has been received rather scornfully by some later philosophers, who have claimed that, aside from the general significance accorded to experiments, the specific aspects of his theory are naive and wrongheaded. Their main criticisms are that Bacon altogether overrated the contribution that observation can make to science, and failed to realize that hypotheses have to play a part in the analysis and interpretation of observations. Bacon is said to have believed that before any explanation is advanced, an exhaustive collection of instances of a phenomenon should be compiled, out of which axioms regarding that phenomenon will somehow emerge, their correctness being ensured by the infallibility of the data.

6(ii) Four Common Criticisms of Bacon's Experimental Philosophy

A number of critics have gone to town on this version (or caricature) of Bacon's philosophy of experiment. First of all, they say that Bacon exaggerated the contribution that facts alone can make to science, and in particular, they criticize his claim that science could be completed, if only a sufficiently comprehensive stock of facts were gathered. Some also object that it would be impossible to collect *all* the facts about any phenomenon, such as heat, for there are simply too many of them. (Some even go so far as to say that their number is infinite.) Next, it has been brought against Bacon that separating fact-collection and the subsequent use of those facts in generating axioms, while perhaps not impossible (though some hold that it is), is not the way that science has actually progressed. In practice, they claim, an investigation proceeds in the reverse order, starting out with a hypothesis, which then determines which facts are relevant, these in turn leading to the confirmation or perhaps the disconfirmation of the original hypothesis. Finally, Bacon is sometimes taken to task for imagining that the factual basis of science could be incorrigible, it being pointed out that observational reports inevitably include some hypothetical, and hence fallible, component.

Although these are powerful objections, they are, I think, unjustly directed at Bacon, whose true position on the character and role of natural histories they seriously misrepresent, as I shall now seek to show.

6(ii a) On the Importance of Histories.   Bacon certainly regarded an appropriate storehouse of facts as an essential prerequisite for any interpretation, describing them as the "foundation of a true philosophy", without whose assistance nothing could be achieved. However, at one point he went further, claiming that, after such an inventory of facts has been accumulated, scientific understanding would be "the work of a few years":

> if all the wits of all the ages had met or shall hereafter meet
> together; if the whole human race had applied or shall
> hereafter apply themselves to philosophy, and the whole
> earth had been or shall be nothing but academies and
> colleges and schools of learned men; still without a natural
> and experimental history such as I am going to prescribe,
> no progress worthy of the human race could have been made

or can be made in philosophy and the sciences. Whereas on
the other hand, let such a history be once provided and well
set forth, and let there be added to it such auxiliary and
light-giving experiments as in the very course of
interpretation will present themselves or will have to be
found out; and the investigation of nature and of all sciences
will be the work of a few years. (*Parasceve ad Historiam et
Naturalem, Works* IV, 252)

The first part of this claim seems unexceptionable. No scientist
would tackle a new area of research without first being thoroughly
versed in the state of the art and the known phenomena of his
subject. For example, a student commencing a doctoral project
would usually start out by making a careful study of the
appropriate scientific literature. The idea that science would be
better served if research were initiated with bold hypotheses is,
pace Popper, a grandiose and quixotic vision not shared by most
practitioners. If the idea ever was entertained seriously, outside
philosophical circles, it must surely have died in the struggle for
scientific survival.

The second point of Bacon's claim, namely, that a suitable
history would suffice to complete the sciences within a few years,
is an extravagant one, however. It is hard to see what could have
persuaded Bacon to it, unless (as is widely believed) he had those
facts in mind as fuel for the fantastic inductive machine already
described and, moreover, he envisaged the end of science as the
correlation of simple natures. On the other hand, it may simply be
a piece of hyperbole to which no special significance should be
attached, an explanation which seems to me to accord better with
Bacon's writings as a whole. Bacon gave no explicit reason for
believing that science could be soon completed and this is,
doubtless, a failing, but it is going too far to dismiss it as plainly or
provenly wrong, as, for example, Popper has done. Popper
inveighed at great length against the idea that science could or
should hope to arrive at "ultimate explanations", but the sole
criticism he assembled against it (1963, 103–7)—that fruitful

questions are prevented from being raised—transparently begs
the question, for if there are fundamental principles, then asking
for a deeper explanation of them will *not* be fruitful. As we have
no idea whether there are ultimate laws of nature or not, the best
policy seems to call for a robust scepticism.

6(ii b) *Should All the Facts be Collected?*   Consider the next
objection. "Facts", Charles Singer pointed out, "are infinite in
number. We cannot choose them all, as Bacon would have had us
do" (1929, 886). Similarly, Dampier considered Bacon's position to
be that "by recording *all* available facts, making *all* possible
observations, performing *all* feasible experiments . . . the
connections between phenomena would become manifest and
general laws describing their relations would emerge almost
automatically" (1929, 137; my italics). And Sorley (1920, 30) stated
that Bacon's method "requires a complete collection of instances,
which in the nature of things is impossible".

It is a mystery why anyone should think that Bacon would
have us record *every* instance before a particular effect could be
interpreted, but it is a view voiced surprisingly often, though, it
must be said, not by most Bacon scholars. After all, Bacon's
intention to depart from the indiscriminate, ant-like accumulation
of facts, which he associated with the "empiric", is one of the most
striking features of his philosophy.

A complete inventory of all the facts is certainly not required
by the mechanical, inductive process frequently attributed to
Bacon, which I described earlier. That method, it will be recalled,
requires one first to analyse a compound body that exhibits the
simple nature we are interested in, into all its constituent simple
natures. Then, by considering other compound bodies, one
discovers the nature which is always copresent with the nature in
question; this being considered the form. Now suppose that a
compound body contains n simple natures, including the one we
are investigating. One would then need to examine at most $n-2$
other compound bodies in order to discover the correct form of

that nature. So, if bodies can be analysed into small numbers of simple natures, the inductive process of elimination proposed in the standard interpretation would require an even smaller number of instances; collecting *every* instance would be quite unnecessary.

When explaining how to collect appropriate data for his investigation into the nature of heat, to which we shall come shortly, Bacon showed that he was well aware that not every instance of heat and cold could be tabulated. Indeed, Bacon's list of instances of cold was not designed to be exhaustive, for, as he said, "to note all these would be endless" (NO II, xii). Instead, he adopted a specific method for selecting among all the possible cases, which we shall examine presently. In a different context, when describing how to discover the causes, symptoms, and remedies of diseases, he commended the Hippocratic practice of setting down a "narrative of the special cases of his patients; relating what was the nature of the disease, what the treatment, and what the issue." But this history should not be "so copious as to extend to every common case of daily occurrence (*for that would be something infinite, and foreign to the purpose*)". (DA 4ii, 384–5; my italics) And Bacon's calendar of hot things was designed to comprise "all known instances which agree in the same nature, *though in substances the most unlike*" (NO II, xi; my italics). In other words, a collection containing only similar instances would not serve; Bacon required, rather, a *variety* of instances, which would share the character in question but which would otherwise be very different. This perceptive requirement is absolutely central to the Baconian principles of natural history.

It is also clear from the general account which Bacon offered of how natural histories ought to be composed that his plan was not to note every single instance, for some—the so-called prerogative instances—have a greater inductive force than others. I shall consider this account in due course.

6(ii c) *The Relation of Theory to Fact.*   Take the third criticism, as voiced for example by W. M. Dickie, who accused Bacon of proposing "a division of labour. Let observers collect facts. Let theorists evolve the laws governing the facts". But, Dickie objected, "modern science has taught that fact and theory cannot be severed in this way. A 'working hypothesis' is necessary. With it we *select* the facts necessary for its proof or disproof" (1922, 485). Ellis raised a similar criticism: "No one acquainted with the history of natural philosophy would think it possible to form a collection of all the facts which are to be the materials on which any science is to operate, antecedently to the formation of the science itself." And Ellis's reason for denying that possibility was primarily that "the observations necessary in order to the recognition of these facts would never have been made except under the guidance of some preconceived idea as to the subject of observation" (1857a, 61). Meyerson (1930, 391) thought Bacon could not be better refuted than by quoting the experimental chemist Bertholet: "To attempt an experiment . . . one must have an end, be guided by an hypothesis."

I believe this criticism, like the last one, to be based on a misunderstanding of Bacon's doctrine, which did not entail a complete divorce between the collection of facts and the inductive process of interpretation. On the contrary, the two were closely connected, in exactly the way one would imagine they should be. I have already pointed out that Bacon did not demand an exhaustive collection of every instance prior to the inductive step; it is also true that he did not even require all the *relevant* particulars to be gathered in advance. Bacon could not have expressed himself more clearly and deliberately when he insisted that the inductive method will go back and forth, using observations to generate hypotheses and hypotheses to generate new observations, and even, as we shall see, to correct old ones:

> the true method of experience . . . first lights the candle, and then by means of the candle shows the way; commencing as it does with experience duly ordered and digested, not bungling or erratic, and from it educing axioms, and from established axioms again new experiments . . . (NO I, lxxxii)

> my course and method, as I have often clearly stated and would wish to state again, is this, — not to extract works from works or experiments from experiments (as an empiric),

but from works and experiments to extract causes and
axioms, and again from those causes and axioms new works
and experiments, as a legitimate interpreter of nature.
(NO I, cxvii)

Moreover, Bacon followed his precepts in practice. For
instance, his theory of heat and cold implies (or so he suggested)
that cold will travel more quickly downward than up, in contrast
with heat, and he designed a simple trial to check this prediction.
The second book of the *Novum Organum* contains numerous
predictions derived from theories which Bacon advanced, and
which he intended should be checked in experiment.

The requirement for an axiom to lead to new particulars,
which should then be verified by experiment, was also the
primary factor distinguishing interpretations from anticipations, as
Bacon defined these. Hence, at least some of the facts involved in
the inductive process must be brought to light by hypothetical
reasoning.

But a number of Bacon's critics have demanded more. *All* such
facts, they have said, must be discovered by the intervention of
some antecedent theory, or "working hypothesis" (in Dickie's
words), for without a prior hypothesis we should never know
which facts to select as relevant. This is plausible reasoning, but
actually a non-sequitur. To be sure, factual statements are
relevant, in the sense of having evidential force, only in relation to
a theory, but this is a *reciprocal* relationship and it is thus also
true that a theory is a relevant explanation only with respect to
certain facts. So we are not entitled to conclude that either theory
or fact has to take precedence in an investigation. The typical
mode in science, where a new area is being investigated, is for
facts to be noted, not through any reflection on causal hypotheses
but merely out of curiosity as to what their causes might be. Then
an explanation is advanced, which in turn directs us to new facts
and these perhaps to a revised theory. This is precisely how Bacon
envisaged it.

6(ii d) On the Corrigibility of Histories.   The fourth charge
sometimes laid against Bacon is that he erroneously assumed that

the facts in his natural histories could be incorrigible. This is part and parcel of the traditional view that, for Bacon, science would be infallible, being constructed out of 'pure' facts, which are impressed on a purified mind and then worked up in some way into necessarily true axioms. Now I have already argued that Bacon did not expect the removal of the idols, in so far as this is possible, to leave the mind a vacant receptacle for immaculate perceptions, unsullied by any kind of interpretation. And I have also criticized the idea that Baconian science was to have been hypothesis-free and infallible. It seems to me that Bacon's views on the nature of those observations which would supply a natural history are all of a piece with the rest of the interpretation that I have offered.

Bacon's natural histories were to consist of three types of data. Some of these would be well-known fallacies, which he thought it would be useful to record, so "that the sciences may be no more troubled with them" and he mentioned various old wives' tales concerning the magnet, which Gilbert had lately exploded, as examples of what he meant. Secondly, uncertain information ought to be included, though with qualifications, such as 'it is reported' or 'they relate', together with a note of the author and origin of the report. Finally, information which is "certainly true" should be "set down simply" and without any elaboration. (*Parasceve ad Historiam et Naturalem, Works* IV, 260) Bacon followed these rules in his own detailed histories.

The question now arises whether the certainty to which Bacon here referred is the certainty of infallibility. A sign that it may be comes from his advice on how to compile a "history of celestial bodies", for this was required to be "simple, and without any infusion of dogmas; all theoretical doctrine being as it were suspended: a history embracing only the phenomena themselves (now almost incorporated with the dogmas) pure and separate". This looks as if Bacon wanted observations which were absolutely theory-free and, hence, absolutely certain and incorrigible. However, the further explanation indicates otherwise. The history, Bacon continued, must set forth a "simple narrative of the facts, just as if nothing had been settled *by the arts of astronomy and*

astrology, and only experiments and observations had been
accurately collected and described with perspicuity" and "the best
history of the celestial bodies . . . might be extracted and worked
out from Ptolemaeus and Copernicus . . . *taking the experiments
detached from the art*" (DIG, 510–11; my italics). The most
plausible reading of this seems to be that factual reports need not
be free of every theoretical presupposition, merely that they
should not presuppose the disputed theories of astronomy and
astrology. This is an eminently reasonable demand, for if those
reports are interpreted according to particular astronomical
theories, then they could not fairly arbitrate between them. We
should expect then that a report that an epicycle pertaining to
some planet has such-and-such a diameter would be disallowed
from a Baconian history, while the facts of whether the stars are
"solid or flamy" or whether the interstellar spaces consist of *"body
or vacuum"* would be welcomed, and in fact they were. (DIG,
515–6)

   We would have better reason to think that Bacon allowed only
infallible observations had he desired to restrict them to what are
sometimes called 'direct' sense-impressions. But there is nothing
of the red-here-now variety in Bacon's natural histories, and he
actually repudiated the idea that his aim could be accomplished
by restricting the empirical foundation to sense-data. First of all,
"very many things in nature . . . escape the sense, even when
best disposed and no way obstructed". Secondly, "when the sense
does apprehend a thing its apprehension is not much to be relied
upon. For the testimony and information of the sense has
reference always to man, not to the universe; and it is a great
error to assert that the sense is the measure of things." (*Plan*, 26)
On the contrary, the natural histories were to report experiments,
for these will "supply [the] . . . failures" of the sense and "correct
its errors":

> For the subtlety of experiments is far greater than that of the
> sense itself, *even when assisted by exquisite instruments;*
> such experiments, I mean, as are skilfully and artificially

devised for the express purpose of determining the point in
question. To the immediate and proper perception of the
sense therefore I do not give much weight; but I contrive that
the office of the sense shall be only to judge of the
experiment, and that the experiment itself shall judge of the
thing. (*Plan*, 26; my italics)

Thus Bacon could not claim infallibility for his histories on the
grounds that they recorded sense-data; in his scheme they were to
contain ordinary reports of experiments, and he does not seem to
have thought that these were incorrigible. On the contrary, in a
statement which was clearly considered carefully, he allowed that
they may even be false and, if so, that they may be corrected in
the course of the induction:

There will be found no doubt, when my history and tables of
discovery are read, some things in the experiments
themselves that are not quite certain, or perhaps that are
quite false; which may make a man think that the foundations
and principles upon which my discoveries rest are false and
doubtful. But this is of no consequence; for such things must
needs happen at first. It is only like the occurrence in a
written or printed page of a letter or two mistaken or
misplaced; which does not much hinder the reader, because
such errors are easily corrected by the sense. So likewise may
there occur in my natural history many experiments which
are mistaken and falsely set down, and yet they will presently
by the discovery of causes and axioms be easily expunged and
rejected. It is nevertheless true that if the mistakes in natural
history and experiments are important, frequent, and
continual, they cannot possibly be corrected or amended by
any felicity of wit or art. (NO I, cxviii)

This shows that, as I have been arguing, Bacon did not believe
that the histories needed to be infallibly true in order for perfectly
satisfactory inductions to be performed upon them. It also
presents the interesting thesis that factual errors will quickly be
expunged, by the discovery of causes, unless they are "important,
frequent, and continual". Though rather vaguely expressed,

Bacon's thesis is, doubtless, broadly true; and his analogy with a page of writing is very apt. If a text has just a few minor typographical errors, it is easy to guess its meaning and thereby to correct its errors; but this would not be nearly so simple if, say, every other letter were misprinted, or if a few key words were indecipherable. The same would seem to apply when one tries to 'read' a portion of nature. If one starts with very imperfect data, one is less likely to arrive at a correct theory and, hence, less likely to be able to rid the data of error.

6(ii e) Summary.   Bacon's method, I contend, is innocent of most of the charges we have considered, the one exception being his exaggerated claim that science would soon be completed by suitably expanding our natural histories. However, Bacon's method did not require *every* instance of a phenomenon to be recorded; it did not banish hypotheses from the process of data collection; and, while the initial survey was to be made without regard to any hypothetical causal explanation of the phenomenon in question, this, as I argued, is the right approach and the critics are in the wrong. Finally, the instances from which an induction is drawn are quite ordinary experimental observations with no pretence to incorrigibility and, indeed, Bacon acknowledged that they may turn out to be false.

6(iii) Constructing the Histories

Bacon insisted that an extensive survey of instances be prepared before any interpretation is attempted. These will be either instances of natural occurrence or else ones that have been artificially created in experiment, often with the express purpose of answering some question that may have arisen. Indeed, "the skilful proposing of *Doubts*" provides a fruitful incentive to the discovery of new and useful instances: "doubts once registered are so many suckers or sponges which continually draw and attract increase of knowledge; whence it comes that things which, if doubts had not preceded, would have been passed by lightly without observation, are through the suggestion of doubts attentively and carefully observed." (DA 3iv, 357–8)

A crucial problem that Bacon needed to face was how histories should be limited, since he knew that it would be impossible and in any case "foreign to the purpose" to list every instance and to answer every conceivable doubt. One of his most interesting suggestions was that a history should record a variety of *heterogeneous* instances. Thus, as was noted earlier, Bacon intended his natural history of heat to contain instances which agree in being hot, but which are "in substances the most unlike". He did not illuminate this remark by delving into the nature of substance, but the same thought was behind another account of natural histories, which proceeded from the assumption that individual objects are naturally grouped into kinds or species. Bacon argued that it is neither necessary nor desirable to note every particular in each species for "since there is in natural objects a promiscuous resemblance one to another, insomuch that if you know one you know all, it would be a superfluous and endless labour to speak of them severally." (DIG, 505) This explanation suggests that his list of hot objects would not call for separate entries relating, for example, to water boiled on Mondays, Tuesdays, etc., for these are so similar that if you know that boiling water is hot on one day of the week, then you would also know that for any other. In such cases, it would suffice simply to list boiling water as an instance where heat is present. As a matter of fact, Bacon broadened the category even further, to encompass boiling liquids in general.

But, as well as mentioning general phenomena like these, a history should also catalogue particular cases which are either unique in their species, or else what he called "monsters" or "prodigies", that is, in some (unspecified) sense, unrepresentative examples of their kind. Bacon mentioned the sun, the moon, and the earth as singletons, which should therefore be entered separately. The monstrous elements contained in a species, such as magnets among stones, should also be dealt with individually because, being so unusual, "a description and knowledge of the species itself is neither sufficient nor competent." (DIG, 505) It seems to be an arbitrary matter whether one regards these singular cases as existing in their own species or as being prodigies within others, and it does not seem to have mattered to Bacon, who sometimes classified the sun and moon as unique constituents of their own classes and sometimes as exceptional instances amongst the wider class of stars (NO II, xxviii).

Bacon took no trouble to defend this doctrine of species and prodigies, which is, perhaps, just as well, for he showed no awareness of the fact that what might seem like a natural grouping of phenomena into a species and what appears to be an unrepresentative instance of such a species are both influenced by one's theoretical point of view. I am thus not inclined to set much value on Bacon's idea, though it has a close affinity with the now widely held theory that objects and phenomena may enjoy an essential similarity, by virtue of belonging to the same so-called natural kinds. Nevertheless, I think Bacon's view is worth recording, as an attempt to account for two aspects of science which are recognised now, but which do not seem to have been noticed until he pointed them out.

These are, first of all, that what we intuitively regard as similar instances—for example, umpteen repetitions of the same experiment—do not, as a rule, count in support of a theory to nearly so great a degree as a variety of different cases. To take L. J. Cohen's apt example, which he advances while explaining the same aspect of Bacon's methodology: "We do not learn much more about the causal powers of arsenic from the fact that women as well as men die after drinking it" (1980, 221). And, as Bacon himself expressed it in his discussion of the idols, axioms are only properly established by "going to and fro to remote and heterogeneous instances", one of the idols of the mind being a reluctance to proceed beyond the familiar and ordinary.

The second novelty in Bacon's discussion lay in his explanation of *why* variety is especially to be valued over the endless recital of similar cases. It is that to mention all similar instances would be superfluous, since "if you know one you know all"; that is to say, by mentioning a single instance one has, in effect, also taken account of the remaining cases in that class. This is, presumably, not true for heterogeneous instances; their character cannot always be confidently known from what has gone before; they will be novel and surprising, so much so that they may, at first, even seem like "miracles of nature" (NO II, xxviii). Bacon called such instances "Singular", or "Irregular" or, borrowing a grammatical term, "Heteroclite", saying that they are "such as exhibit bodies in the concrete, which seem to be out of the course and broken off from the order of nature, and not agreeing with other bodies of the same kind" (NO II, xxviii).

Bacon did not advance a comprehensive solution to the knotty problem of what makes for variety in observations, nor did he explain exactly why such variety should be especially prized in induction. However, the remarks he did venture are highly pertinent and contain a good deal of truth. While there is no unanimous modern view, this much seems to be agreed: first, the inductive force of evidence depends upon its probability, or the degree to which it is expected in the light of other information; in particular, the more confidently an observation is expected, the less power it has to confirm. This is why a soothsayer's vague and unsurprising prediction that you will, sometime, meet a dark stranger, or go on a journey, usually fails to impress even if it turns out to be true. On the other hand, a very precise, quantitative prediction, which we had no strong prior reason to think was true, would normally be considered powerful evidence for the theory from which it was derived, if it is verified in experiment.

Secondly, in line with Bacon's idea that observations are similar insomuch that if you know one you know all, the modern view is that an important element characterising uniformity in evidence is the degree to which knowledge of one part of it raises the probability of another. Suppose two observations are very similar in this sense and that the first is made practically certain by the second. Then, in view of the inverse dependence that the confirming power of evidence bears to its probability, the second observation will confirm a hypothesis comparatively little. On the other hand, if the observations are diverse, the probability of the one is largely independent of the other. Suppose the observations are also improbable—Bacon described such instances as "prodigies" and as seeming like "miracles of nature"—then *both* support appropriate hypotheses. Bacon's distinction between similar and heterogeneous instances thus resembles the modern one, both in its character and in the significance for inductive reasoning that he attached to it.

6(iv) Prerogative Instances

Apart from the very general guidelines already described for what should be included in a natural history, Bacon offered an elaborate description of the various types of instance which he thought would be particularly useful. These were called "prerogative instances", for they possess special rights and powers in the interpretation of nature; they are "as a soul amid the common instances of Presentation, and . . . a few of them do instead of many" (NO II, lii).

6(iv a) Prerogative Instances Useful for the Initial Survey of Phenomena.   Some of these are clearly related to the doctrine of species, described earlier. Instances which Bacon called "Singular", "Deviating", "Bordering", "Magic", and instances of "Power" are specific types of unusual or extraordinary phenomena. For example, the sun and moon are *Singular* instances of stars. The letter S is singular "on account of its easy combination with consonants, sometimes with two, sometimes even with three; which property no other letter has" (NO II, xxviii). The hope Bacon expressed was that unusual instances, which might at first seem miraculous, will in the end

> be reduced and comprehended under some Form or fixed
> Law; so that all the irregularity or singularity shall be found

to depend on some common Form, and the miracle shall turn
out to be only in the exact specific differences, and the
degree, and the rare concurrence; not in the species itself;
whereas now the thoughts of men go no further than to
pronounce such things the secrets and mighty works of
nature, things as it were causeless, and exceptions to general
rules. (NO II, xxviii)

Bacon also administered advice on what particularly to note when
making observations for a history. Thus, the four Mathematical
Instances, which I detailed in the last chapter, are ones which
report the quantitative aspects of phenomena.

The five *Instances of the Lamp* are, in general, indirect
observations of processes that would, otherwise, be difficult or
impossible to detect directly. Thus, some *(Instances of the Door)*
involve observations conducted by means of various instruments,
such as microscopes, telescopes, astrolabes, etc. Other examples
are observations of the pulse and the urine to gauge the internal
condition of the human body indirectly, and measurements made
with air-thermometers to detect otherwise imperceptible
temperature changes. (These are *Summoning Instances*.) Bacon
also included observations on the detailed course of development
of natural processes, such as the hatching of eggs, among
instances of the Lamp (these are *Instances of the Road*).
Supplementary instances of the Lamp are "those which supply
information when the senses entirely fail us . . . either by gradual
approximation or by analogy". Thus, although no known medium
interposed between a magnet and a piece of iron will deaden the
magnetic attraction, "yet by nice tests some medium may possibly
be found to deaden its virtue more than any other; comparatively,
that is, and in some degree". (NO II, xlii) Similarities, or analogies
may also provide information about invisible processes. For
instance, the interaction between common air and pneumatic
bodies might be studied via analogous mixtures of oil and water or
air and water. Bacon was very conscious of the power of analogies
in science and, as we shall see, he devoted another prerogative
instance entirely to them. However, Bacon warned that, while

analogies are "doubtless useful, [they are] less certain, and should therefore be applied with some judgment". (NO II, xlii)

Finally, *Awakening Instances* of the Lamp are ones that "remind the understanding of the wonderful and exquisite subtlety of nature", an example being that a "little saffron tinges a whole hogshead of water" (NO II, xliii). This is an observation which Bacon cited occasionally as powerful evidence that the ultimate particles of matter are much smaller than those of even the finest powders. (*Thoughts on the Nature of Things, Works* V, 419)

6(iv b) Prerogative Instances Useful for the Induction of Axioms.   The instances we have dealt with illustrate how and in what detail observations should be sought, especially those which will form part of the initial survey of a subject. Other prerogative instances are more closely related to the induction of axioms. For example, those of *Alliance* and of *Divorce* are observations that refute theories.

Instances of *Alliance* show that "effects attributed to some one heterogeneous nature as peculiar to it, may belong also to other heterogeneous natures; so that this supposed heterogeneity is proved to be not real or essential, but only a modification of a common nature" (NO II, xxxv). Bacon's main example concerns heat, which was reputed in Bacon's time (he informs us) to be of three different kinds, viz., the heat of heavenly bodies, of animals, and of fire. This is refuted by the fact that grapes are ripened by fire as well as by the sun. (NO II, xxxv) A more modern example of an instance of Alliance is Wöhler's discovery that urea can be synthesised from inorganic materials, thus refuting the notion of essential heterogeneity between inorganic and so-called organic matter.

Instances of *Divorce* enable one to "notify the separability of one nature from another", "to detect false forms, and to dissipate slight theories suggested by what lies on the surface". Bacon exemplified them with a theory he attributed to Telesius (1508–88), that heat and brightness are constantly conjoined "as messmates and chamber-fellows". This is refuted by the case of the moon, which is cool but bright and by boiling water, which is hot yet dull. (NO II, xxxvii)

Some of the other instances may be helpful in discovering the structure of a system or in arriving at or suggesting the correct axiom or form. Instances of *Analogy*, for example, are appropriate for the first two of these aims; they are cases such as a looking-glass and the eye, the roots and the branches of trees, and the teeth of land animals and the beaks of birds. Bacon held these to be "very serviceable in revealing the fabric of the parts of the universe, and anatomising its members; from which they often lead us along to sublime and noble axioms, especially those which relate to the configuration of the world" (NO II, xxvii). But it is not clear how analogous phenomena will lead to those noble axioms of which Bacon spoke, for he described no direct and identifiable path between them. Indeed, there seems not to be one, in the light of Bacon's "strict and earnest caution, that those only are to be taken for Conformable and Analogous Instances which indicate . . . . Physical Resemblances; that is, real and substantial resemblances; resemblances grounded in nature, not accidental or merely apparent" (NO II, xxvii). But, as he provided no criteria for distinguishing real from imaginary or accidental resemblances, the most he could legitimately have claimed is that they may be very suggestive to the theoretician, and that, beyond this heuristic role, they have little probative power. (Bacon suggested elsewhere, however, that analogies may "corroborate the information" supplied by more direct instances; see page 181 below.) This is, perhaps, a rather muted position to arrive at, especially after the flourish with which the instances of Analogy were announced, which seemed to promise more, but it is at least correct, as the history of science amply shows, and, so far as I am aware, it was an original observation.

Another group of instances towards which Bacon had a rather ambivalent attitude are the *Striking* (also called *Shining*) instances. Their initial characterisation gives the impression that simply contemplating them will lead inevitably to a correct axiom.

They are instances "which exhibit the nature in question naked and standing by itself, and also in its exaltation or highest degree of power" (NO II, xxiv). Examples are boiling or simmering liquids, which are Striking instances of heat, by virtue of being in "perpetual motion" and thus exhibiting the form of heat (which also involves motion) more conspicuously than other instances. Bacon spoke as if some phenomena really manifest the cause which is being sought, in a rather literal way, so that one could simply cast around for a Striking instance of an effect and read off, or directly perceive, its form. But it is clear that instances do not present themselves appropriately labelled, and one could determine whether or not an instance is Striking only if the form itself were already known. Bacon was evidently not unaware of this difficulty, and his words of caution rather take the sting (and some of the interest!) out of his theory, for he warned the reader not to jump to conclusions when looking at what appear to be Striking instances, for one can easily be misled:

> At the same time in these instances also we must use caution, and check the hurry of the understanding. For whatever [seemingly—P.U.] displays the Form too conspicuously, and seems to force it on the notice of the understanding, should be held suspect, and recourse be had to a rigid and careful exclusion. (NO II, xxiv)

Rather similar to his Striking instances are the *Solitary* instances. Bacon described these as "exhibit[ing] the nature under investigation in subjects which have nothing in common with other subjects except that nature" (NO II, xxii). He offered prisms as examples of Solitary instances in the study of colour, for these "show colours not only in themselves but externally on a wall, dews, etc.", explaining further that "they have nothing in common with the colours fixed in flowers, coloured stones, metals, woods, etc., except the colour." It is, of course, an exaggeration to say that the *only* common element in these various bodies is their colour, though perhaps Bacon thought it the only relevant one. At any rate, he said that "we easily gather [from these observations] that colour is nothing more than a modification of the image of light received upon the object", which in turn depends on "the different degrees of incidence" of the light in the case of prisms and, for the other bodies, on their "various textures and configurations" (NO II, xxii). Though Bacon's conclusions were surprisingly accurate and, in outline, anticipated Newton's theory of colour, his discussion of this particular prerogative instance was rather sketchy.

Instances of the *Fingerpost* or *Crucial* Instances constitute Bacon's most famous contribution to the description and classification of experiments. They are distinguished from those other instances, which just refute a hypothesis, by the fact that they also establish one. This happens when "in the investigation of any nature the understanding is so balanced as to be uncertain to which of two or more natures the cause of the nature in question should be assigned". In such cases, "Instances of the Fingerpost show the union of one of the natures with the nature in question to be sure and indissoluble" (NO II, xxxvi).

That is, I believe, Bacon's clearest intimation that one might sometimes be in a position to list a complete set of alternative theoretical possibilities, all but one of which can be refuted. In this respect, instances of the Fingerpost support the interpretation traditionally ascribed to Bacon. However, in analysing the theoretical possibilities in his examples, Bacon did not try to resolve concrete events into congeries of simple natures. Instead, the instances of the Fingerpost were applied to cases where logic alone seems to have determined two distinct possible explanations, one just being the negation of the other. For example, in the question of weight or heaviness, "It must needs be that heavy and weighty bodies either tend of their own nature to the centre of the earth . . . or else that they are attracted by the mass and body of the earth itself". Other examples: the nature of the moon is either "rare, consisting of flame or air . . . or dense and solid"; the motion of projectiles through the air is either caused "by the air carrying the projected body and collecting behind it" or "by the parts of the body itself . . . pushing forward"; and the diurnal rotation of the earth is either "a real motion of rotation in the heavenly bodies, or a motion apparent in the heavenly bodies, and real in the earth". Bacon seems to have thought that these pairs of explanations for the different phenomena were mutually exclusive and exhaustive and, superficially at least, they appear to be. However, there are other possibilities for explaining, for example, the weightiness of bodies than that they are attracted by the earth or that they "tend [to it] of their own nature"; they could be pushed by angels, or tugged by leprechauns. These alternative explanations are, of course, not serious contenders but they demonstrate that Bacon's singling out just two possibilities cannot be defended on logical grounds alone. This fact seems to have forced itself upon him when he attempted to determine the cause of the tides. Bacon drew back from the initial sanguine claim that: "This motion *must necessarily* be caused either by the advance and retreat of the waters; as water shaken in a basin leaves one side when it washes the other; or else by a lifting up of the waters from the bottom and falling again; as water in boiling rises and falls." (NO II, xxxvi; my italics) For, after considering some of the evidence, he noticed that the crucial experiment he first described cannot be decisive, as there is a third possibility, namely that tides may be caused by a progressive motion of waters, parallel to both banks; and he later admitted that the rotation of the earth might also produce the tidal phenomena, as Galileo had suggested.

Bacon's crucial instance for determining the nature of weight is a famous one and it led Voltaire, in 1734, to attribute the discovery of gravity to him and to lavish fulsome praise on Bacon for having, with great sagacity, originated "that attraction of which Newton passes for the inventor". This is something of an exaggeration, as Bacon never disguised his debt to Gilbert for the idea and, by his own report, it seems to have been in the air anyway, for he tells us (in the *Sylva Sylvarum*, 353–4) of its being "affirmed constantly by many, as an usual experiment, that a lump of ore in the bottom of a mine will be tumbled and stirred by two men's strength, which if you bring it to the top of the earth, will ask six men's strength at the least to stir it." He then says that this

"is a noble instance, and is fit to be tried to the full." Bacon's
interesting experiment was designed to do just this.

> Take a clock moved by leaden weights, and another moved by
> the compression of an iron spring; let them be exactly
> adjusted, that one go not faster or slower than the other; then
> place the clock moving by weights on the top of a very high
> steeple, keeping the other down below; and observe carefully
> whether the clock on the steeple goes more slowly than it
> did, on account of the diminished virtue of its weights.
> Repeat the experiment in the bottom of a mine, sunk to a
> great depth below the ground; that is, observe whether the
> clock so placed does not go faster than it did, on account of
> the increased virtue of its weights. (NO II, xxxvi)

Now Bacon argued that if bodies are attracted to the earth, "it
follows that the nearer heavy bodies approach to the earth, the
more rapid and violent is their motion to it; and that the further
they are from the earth, the feebler and more tardy is their
motion (as is the case with magnetic attraction)". The experiment
may enable us to arrive at a definite conclusion as to the cause of
heaviness, for: "If the virtue of the weights is found to be
diminished on the steeple, and increased in the mine, we may
take the attraction of the mass of the earth as the cause of weight."
(It is to be noted that the effect of being lowered into a mine on
the weight of a body, which Bacon predicted here, is the exact
opposite to the extraordinary story to which he gave serious
attention in the *Sylva Sylvarum*.)

6 (iv c) Summary.   Bacon's classification of the various types of
experiment (twenty-seven in all) and his discussion of the
information that might be drawn from them was an almost entirely
original contribution to the philosophy of science, which,
unfortunately, has been little pursued by later philosophers.
Hacking (1984, 159) has described Bacon, rightly, as "the first and
almost last philosopher of experiments".

Unlike most of his predecessors, who also pressed for a more
empirical approach to the acquisition of knowledge, Bacon

attempted to supply details and to set an example. The prerogative instances are also interesting in that they demonstrate that not all observations are of equal weight in the inductive process; that some indeed do not have a significant probative role but are heuristically useful; and that there is a need for precise and varied observations. Bacon's commentary, in which examples of contemporary scientific interest were cited, was sometimes amateurish and laboured and, perhaps, a little boring to modern readers; but it is often also perceptive and original, and it is remarkable that, with so little science to go on, Bacon achieved so much.

6(v) The Tables of Instances and the Example of Heat

The most famous example of Bacon's method in action is his investigation into the nature of heat. This begins, as he always recommended, with a natural history, which for this purpose was ranged into tables. The tabular method was not propounded as a new inductive technique but was adopted for convenience, in order "that the understanding may be able to deal with them [the instances], for "natural and experimental history is so various and diffuse, that it confounds and distracts the understanding, unless it be ranged and presented to view in a suitable order." (NO II, x)

The first table describes "Instances Agreeing in the Nature of Heat", the second lists those where that nature is absent, and the third, called a "Table of Degrees", contains cases in which "the nature under inquiry is found in different degrees". Bacon also mentioned a "Table of Degrees of Cold", but this played no part in his investigation of heat.

The first table should exhibit "all known instances" where heat is manifested, but with the proviso that they shall be "in substances the most unlike", a requirement whose meaning we have already explored. The list of cold things must also be composed selectively, and Bacon's principle for including a particular instance was that "the absence of the given nature [should be] inquired of in those subjects only that are most akin to the others in which it is present". The following, which retains the original numbering, is a part of Bacon's tables so constituted.

Instances Agreeing in the Nature of Heat	Instances . . . where the Nature of Heat is Absent
1. The rays of the sun . . .	The rays of the moon . . .
2. The rays of the sun reflected and condensed, as between mountains . . . and most of all in burning-glasses [convex lenses] and mirrors.	The reflexion of the rays of the sun in regions near the polar circles . . . [At this point Bacon suggested various experiments to see whether the moon's rays can be collected and made warm by convex lenses, whether the radiant heat of flames and hot bodies is condensed by such lenses, and whether concave lenses diminish the heat of the sun by spreading it out, as it does light.]
9. Liquids boiling or heated.	Liquid itself in its natural state. For we find no tangible liquid which is warm in its own nature and remains so constantly . . .
14. All bodies . . . held for a time near the fire.	To this no Negative is subjoined. For there is nothing found among us either tangible or spirituous which does not contract warmth when put near fire.
21. Horse-dung and like excrements of animals when fresh.	To this Instance it is hard to subjoin a Negative. Indeed, the excrements of animals when no longer fresh have manifestly a potential heat, as is seen in the enriching of soil.
28. Other instances.	

Bacon detailed twenty-seven cases in all, leaving the tables incomplete. Nevertheless, he felt entitled to draw certain negative conclusions from them. For instance, because gold and other metals are sometimes very hot, we may, he said, "reject rarity" (i.e., tenuousness) as a possible element in the form of heat. But rarity can also be rejected "On account of air, which is found for the most part cold and yet remains rare" (NO II, xviii). Bacon was quite explicit about what he was doing here. A form is both a necessary and a sufficient condition for a particular phenomenon. Hence, if F is conjectured to be the form of P, we shall be able to reject that conjecture if we find an instance that is either F but not P, or P but not F. This is how he explained the principle:

> when I say (for instance) in the investigation of the form of heat, "reject rarity," or "rarity does not belong to the form of heat," it is the same as if I said, "It is possible to superinduce heat on a dense body;" or, "It is possible to take away or keep out heat from a rare body." (NO II, xvii)

So when Bacon rejected rarity from the form of heat, he was ruling it out, first of all, as a necessary condition, and, secondly, as a sufficient condition, for he based those rejections, respectively, on a hot but dense body (heated gold) and on a cool but rare body (cold air). This might seem like overkill, but Bacon explained that he sometimes multiplied an exclusion "for clearness' sake", and so that "the use of the tables may be more plainly shown" (NO II, xviii).

One feature of the tables is not explained, though, namely why it is desirable to connect negatives to positive instances with which they are "most akin". Bacon argued that it follows from the need to limit the table, for to note every instance of cold would be endless. But why did he not adopt the principle already approved for the selection of the phenomena of heat, namely that of choosing a wide variety of instances? This would also have produced the desired result of restricting attention to a more manageable range of negative instances. It could, perhaps, be argued that the method Bacon adopted does apply the earlier selection principle, though in a roundabout way, for, since the instances of heat are all very different from one another, matching each of them with an instance where heat is absent necessarily produces a set of correspondingly heterogeneous instances of cold. Bacon's method of composing his history could then be defended on the grounds of convenience or symmetry. However, this plausible, though by no means watertight, argument was not even hinted at by Bacon.

Another, more likely, possibility is this. Bacon employed the instances of the presence of heat as material for rejecting possible *necessary* conditions for heat. Thus, light and brightness were rejected from the form of heat in view of boiling water, which is hot but dull. Also, "local or expansive motion of the body as a whole" was rejected "On account of ignited iron, which does not swell in bulk" (NO II, xviii). But the positive instances of a phenomenon may play another role in Bacon's tables, namely as sources of conjectures about *sufficient* conditions. Thus, if we observe heat in a body which also displays the nature S, we might be led to hypothesise that S is sufficient for producing heat. The proper method of testing this hypothesis is to examine other cases where S is present. If one is found which is not hot, then it will be entered in the second table and lead to a rejection of S as a sufficient condition for heat, in the way that Bacon did. The table of negative instances may then be formed on the principle that it include observations generated in the course of testing specific hypotheses, in particular, those that have been suggested by items listed in the table of presence. This would explain why Bacon did not specify that the former table should contain all known instances of cold, as he had done (with of course the proviso that the instances should be "in substances the most unlike"), in the corresponding case of heat. It would explain, too, why the negative instances should be matched with an appropriate positive instance.

This explanation also finds support from specific entries in the Table of Absence, where directions for several new experiments are given, whose inspiration clearly derived from an associated positive instance. The idea of checking whether radiant heat is

"condensed" (i.e., focussed) by a burning-glass and whether cool
rays can be made warm by such a glass are cases in point.
Similarly, the positive instance of warm air confined in a cavern in
winter is connected with the negative instance of air trapped in
caverns in the summer, which Bacon said is cold. But he was
uncertain of whether these temperature variations were
attributable to the confinement, or to the communication of heat
or cold from outside. Accordingly, he suggested that air held for a
few days in an insulated and sealed flask be tested by hand or
probed with a thermometer (a "graduated glass"). Another
example: in the slot in the Table of Absence corresponding to the
instances of heat of "villous substances, [such] as wool, skins of
animals, and down of birds", Bacon remarked that "a doubt
suggests itself, whether the warmth in wool, skins, feathers, and
the like, proceeds from a faint degree of heat inherent in them
. . . or from a certain fat and oiliness, which is of a nature akin to
warmth; or simply, as surmised in the preceding article
[concerning air trapped in caverns], from the confinement and
separation of the air" (NO II, xii, item 19). He then proposed that
fibrous material not derived from any animal source, such as
linen, should be examined for its warmth. Other materials, such
as powders, "in which there is manifestly air enclosed", should
also be observed to see whether they "are less cold than the
whole substances they are made from" (NO II, xii, item 19).

6(vi) Tables of Degrees

As well as the two tables described, Bacon required another,
in which substances that exhibit heat in different degrees would
be noted. Bacon argued that

> since the Form of a thing is the very thing itself, and the
> thing differs from the form no otherwise than as the apparent
> differs from the real, or the external from the internal, or the
> thing in reference to man from the thing in reference to the
> universe; it necessarily follows that no nature can be taken as

the true form, unless it always decrease when the nature in question decreases, and in like manner always increase when the nature in question increases. (NO II, xiii)

This aspect of forms is an innovation in Bacon's discussion of the matter and it rather confuses the simple picture of them as necessary and sufficient conditions for a corresponding nature, which Bacon presented elsewhere. Heat is a nature that manifests itself in differing degrees, and it is natural to assume, as Bacon did, that the causes of various heat states are also graduated on a single, natural scale. It is conceivable, however, that this might not have been the case; that, for example, a temperature of 80° C in water is caused by a certain agitation of its particles, but that 85° C can be reached if and only if a specific caloric fluid is present. Bacon's new characterisation of forms excludes this possibility, though he gave no argument to justify its exclusion. In the case of heat, Bacon's view is no doubt very plausible, but as a general principle it cannot be accepted, for one is often quite unsure whether certain effects are essentially the same phenomena appearing in various grades or whether they have quite different causal antecedents, and much of the inductive process may be directed to resolving precisely this question. Indeed, in Bacon's own time there was uncertainty about whether heat and cold stood at opposite ends of a single spectrum or whether they were essentially different kinds of phenomena. For instance, Descartes remarked (in 1641) that the ideas which he had of cold and heat were "so far from clear and distinct that by their means I cannot tell whether cold is merely a privation of heat, or heat a privation of cold, or whether both are real qualities, or are not such" *(Third Meditation).*

The Table of Degrees of heat was compiled in a haphazard way with no explicit principle of selection being expounded, though its forty-one entries seem to comply with the rule to choose a wide variety of instances. Here are a few of his examples.

> 9. Animals increase in heat by motion and exercise, wine, feasting, venus, burning fevers, and pain.

16. The sun gives greater heat the nearer he approaches to the perpendicular or zenith; and this is probably true of the other planets also . . .

21. There are . . . many degrees of strength and weakness in the heat of flame and ignited bodies. But as they have never been diligently inquired into, we must pass them lightly over. [There follows a brief survey of cases, from the cool flame of wine to the intense heat of burning pitch.]

27. Motion increases heat, as you may see in bellows, and by blowing . . .

37. There are many degrees in susceptibility of heat . . . it is to be observed how slight and faint a heat changes and somewhat warms even those bodies which are least of all susceptible of heat.

Bacon used these instances to exclude some possible causes of heat. For example, "On account of the ease with which all bodies are heated, without any destruction or observable alteration", he decided to "reject a destructive nature" (NO II, xviii).

6(vii) The Commencement of Interpretation, or the First Vintage

So far, a variety of natures, which might belong to the form of heat, have been considered and rejected by means of the instances ranged in the three tables. Investigations such as these, though, have a more positive goal, namely to discover what the cause or causes of the phenomena in question actually are: As Bacon put it, "In the process of Exclusion are laid the foundations of true Induction, which however is not completed till it arrives at an Affirmative." Bacon added, moreover, that the exclusive part is not complete, "nor indeed can it possibly be so at first. For Exclusion is evidently the rejection of simple natures; and if we do not yet possess sound and true notions of simple natures, how can the process of Exclusion be made accurate?" (NO II, xix)

This sounds as if Bacon thought the inductive process would proceed, at least ideally, via a number of rejections, and, when completed, would arrive at a single remaining possibility, which would perforce be the correct one, and that the only hindrance lay in the inadequacy of our conceptions of simple natures. That is, the standard interpretation seems to be supported. However, it is also consistent with there being two parts to the inductive process: an exclusive part and a more positive, affirmative, part, with only the first of these being uncompletable. This two-part process would explain why Bacon said, in the quotation above, that "In the process of exclusion are laid the *foundations* of true induction" (my emphasis), thereby suggesting that the superstructure must be built out of different materials. And, as we shall see presently, Bacon did introduce another part to the process of induction.

The earlier gloss, favourable to the standard interpretation, gets some extra backing, however, from another of Bacon's claims, made in the midst of his investigation of heat, namely, that, "after the rejection and exclusion has been duly made, there will remain at bottom, all light opinions vanishing into smoke, a Form affirmative, solid and true and well defined" (NO II, xvi). But he straight away added that while "This is quickly said . . . the way to come at it is winding and intricate", and it turns out that this way involves something more than mere rejections of simple observable properties. Bacon introduced the next stage in the induction with a famous remark, in which he said:

> since truth will sooner come out from error than from confusion, I think it expedient that the understanding should have permission, after the three Tables of First Presentation (such as I have exhibited) have been made and weighed, to make an essay of the Interpretation of Nature in the affirmative way; on the strength both of the instances given in the tables, and of any others it may meet with elsewhere.
> (NO II, xx)

Bacon dubbed this next stage in the induction the "Indulgence of the Understanding", or the "Commencement of Interpretation", or the "*First Vintage* concerning the form of heat".

Bacon's first surmise was that "the nature of which Heat is a particular case appears to be Motion", a conclusion arrived at after surveying various Shining instances, such as boiling water, simmering liquids, flames, and the manner in which a bellows increases the heat of a fire. This theory is refined in the light of numerous other items in the tables and, in its final version, heat is connected with a certain type of motion, in particular:

> Heat is a motion, expansive, restrained, and acting in its
> strife upon the smaller particles of bodies. But the expansion
> is thus modified; while it expands all ways, it has at the same
> time an inclination upwards. And the struggle in the particles
> is modified also; it is not sluggish, but hurried and with
> violence. (NO II, xx; original italics removed)

There are a number of interesting points about this conclusion. First, it was not considered conclusive or infallible by Bacon. This is clear from the warning which he appended to his discussion of Shining instances and which we discussed earlier (pp. 167–168 above), that the information they can impart is precarious and "should be held suspect" and also from the necessity he perceived of augmenting the First Vintage with "other helps of the understanding". Bacon referred to nine such supplementary measures, but he got round to describing only one of them in any detail, namely the prerogative instances.

The observations and experimental results listed as examples of prerogative instances were not all new, however, for many of them already appeared in the tables. Indeed, Bacon intended that "in the formation of the Tables they must be investigated with zeal, and set down therein" (NO II, lii). Bacon's discussion was designed, then, not to describe some additional inductive technique but to elaborate general categories of observations and to explain how and why they are notable, and possess special prerogatives. Oddly enough, the number of prerogative instances exactly matches the number of types of positive instances of heat that Bacon lists, but this is surely a coincidence.

conclusion after taking the view that Bacon intended infallible theories to spring fully-formed and automatically from the tables. But, as I have argued, this untenable assumption constituted no part of Bacon's plan and, without it, his theory is perfectly reasonable and correct.

There is little or no evidence that he ever designed his histories to be composed of infallible facts, nor that they were to be exhaustive lists of every instance of a phenomenon. Bacon's advice was remarkably sensible. He said that one should survey the relevant facts of a phenomenon in the early stages of trying to understand it, and this is what scientists, in fact, do, for they proceed on the natural assumption that it is useful to know something about a phenomenon before speculating on its underlying causal structure. The suggestion that this preliminary survey is best performed in an organised way via tables is, surely, harmless enough.

Bacon was aware that information is more readily yielded from a wide range of heterogeneous instances and his conception of variety had much truth and originality in it. So far as I have been able to determine, the idea that variety among instances is of the first importance in induction had not been made before, and it was certainly overlooked by very many philosophers dealing with scientific method until this century.

The idea that an investigation should commence by considering what easily detectable properties are correlated with the one in question is surely reasonable too, and it is evidently the initial step of much modern research, for example, into the causes of cancer. This preliminary survey will thus, normally, produce a schedule of negative instances similar to Bacon's second table.

The next stage in Bacon's method, the First Vintage, had the task of discovering the form of a given nature and therefore involved speculating on its latent causal structure. I have argued, and believe I have shown, that this was not an eleventh-hour expedient forced on Bacon, throwing his philosophy into disarray, but was foreshadowed and implied by his philosophy.

The nature of the rest of the other helps has to be surmised primarily from their names. These are the "Supports of Induction", the "Rectification of Induction", "Varying the Investigation according to the natures of the Subject", "Prerogative Natures with respect to Investigation" ("or of what should be inquired first and what last"), the "Limits of Investigation" ("or a Synopsis of all Natures in the Universe"), the "Application to Practice" (or "things in their relation to Man"), "Preparations for Investigation", and the "Ascending and Descending Scale of Axioms". (NO II, xxi)

Bacon provided a few hints on what should appear under some of these heads. Thus, the Supplementary instances, included among the prerogative instances of the Lamp, are observations indirectly related to the phenomena under study, as analogues. (They are discussed on pages 165–167 above.) Bacon said of these that they are a "last resource" when we cannot observe the phenomena directly, though even when "proper instances" are available they are still of great utility in "corroborating the information which the others supply" (NO II, xlii). These instances are evidently connected with the Supports of Induction, as he promised to treat of them more fully under that title. Bacon also referred briefly to Applications to Practice (whose meaning is fairly obvious from the name) when dealing with certain of the prerogative instances ("Intimating" instances), which, he said, serve to "intimate or point out what is useful to man" (NO II, xlix). A similar topic was also touched on in the *De Augmentis*, under the title of "Application of Experiment", where "the ingenious translation of . . . [one experiment] to some other useful experiment" is discussed, and exemplified by Archimedes' analysis of the king's crown, through a knowledge of the densities of gold and silver. (DA 4ii, 419)

6(viii) The Role and Purpose of the First Vintage

While Bacon drew his conclusion about the form of heat only tentatively, this is not to say that the First Vintage introduced

In summary, then, Bacon's contribution to experimental philosophy went very much further than the vague advice that experiment and observation should figure more prominently in induction, advice which had already been proffered by other philosophers of the time. Bacon well deserves his title of "Father of Experimental Philosophy" because of the accuracy of his conception of the empirical basis of knowledge and the detail with which he expounded it.

Chapter Seven
Conclusion

> . . . *it may be objected to me*
> *with truth, that my words*
> *require an age; a whole age*
> *perhaps to prove them, and*
> *many ages to perfect them. But*
> *yet as even the greatest things*
> *are owing to their beginnings, it*
> *will be enough for me to have*
> *sown a seed for posterity . . .*
> (DA 9i, 119)

Interpreting the ideas of a philosopher is a difficult task, especially when he wrote as much and as variedly as Bacon did. For, over many volumes, a person is almost bound to contradict himself, either through accidental slips or because his ideas have altered and developed, or simply as a result of failing to understand the implications of his own thesis. How then is one to discover what a philosopher *really* meant? Indeed, under such circumstances, is it even meaningful to talk of the 'real' meaning behind a philosophical text?

I will not attempt to answer this question in its general form, but instead will restate my plan in interpreting Bacon, which was to try to extract a consistent position from the widest range of those statements to which Bacon seems to have attached the greatest importance. I think it wrong to be unfairly biased towards the most interesting or modern-sounding interpretations that can be wrung out of a philosopher's words; this would be like the tendency in some modern literature to be prepared to mix fact and fiction, with the aim of pursuing an extraneous train of thought or wishful thinking. Nevertheless, I think that Bacon's position, as it emerges from the present analysis, is both interesting and modern, and that Bacon would have recognised it as his own.

In expounding Bacon's thought, I was influenced by the conviction that he was a brilliant and perceptive thinker, and by the knowledge that his philosophical reflections were not merely dashed off in-between affairs of state but were usually delivered in their final form only after long thought. Bacon's perceptiveness seems to me manifest on practically every page of his writings, and the many drafts that we have of his various ideas show clearly that he had mulled over them for many years.

These two facts seem to me to make most implausible the central claim of what I have called the 'standard' interpretation of Bacon, namely that he thought his method infallible. For one thing, sceptical arguments implying that there could be no such method were simple and persuasive and almost certainly well-known to Bacon. Secondly, if Bacon had wanted to base his method on the various assumptions set out by Mary Hesse, or on some other set of assumptions, he could hardly have failed to notice that any claim to infallibility would lead to an infinite regress of justifications. For he argued several times against the syllogism, as a tool of discovery, on the grounds that it could not endorse the conclusions drawn from it unless its premises were secured; it would be extraordinary had he forgotten this warning in respect of his own conclusions.

There is more direct evidence that Bacon did not base himself on the infallibility thesis. First, he himself never described the axioms delivered by his method as infallible, merely as "certain" or "proved" or "demonstrated", none of which terms seems to have carried the connotation of necessary or necessarily true.

Proofs and demonstrations, as I argued in Chapter Two, did not signify impossible transformations of synthetic statements into necessarily true ones; they were, rather, confirmations or corroborations, which excite belief or render a thesis more convincing and, with many such proofs, eventually so convincing that it is considered practically certain.

Secondly, if Baconian axioms had been envisaged as infallible, they would have had to proceed from infallible observations, but we are told explicitly that the factual foundation of an induction may well contain mistakes and yet not be vitiated. Moreover, the facts out of which histories were to be compiled were not direct reports of sensations, which might conceivably have some claim to incorrigibility, but were perfectly ordinary observations, and reports of the outcomes of experiments.

A third point against the infallibility interpretation is that Bacon did not criticize the established sciences for being fallible. The commonest objection was that they failed to employ a genuinely empirical method whereby their theories would be experimentally tested and, if necessary, replaced, but instead set up principles which "stand like statues, worshipped and celebrated, but not moved or advanced" (Preface to *The Great Instauration, Works* IV, 14). The way of many natural philosophers, Bacon said, was then carefully to shield those principles from any kind of criticism, either by ignoring or by reinterpreting adverse evidence. Astronomers supplied a particularly clear case of this sort of reasoning, for their basic hypotheses were explicitly rendered invulnerable to revision from new facts, by a declaration that they were merely conventions, or rules, for organising the known phenomena.

When Bacon disparaged speculation or conjectures, he was not, I contend, objecting to hypotheses themselves; he was warning against the danger that speculations may be vested with a spurious security through the various rescue devices which he described and be treated as inviolate truths. Bacon was also concerned lest particular speculations should be *mere* conjectures, rashly induced and ill-supported by evidence.

Horton, in criticism of Bacon, said that "many scientific hypotheses are over-hasty generalizations from insufficient evidence, *and are none the worse hypotheses because of it*" (1973, 250; my italics). But this seems to me a symptom of the Popperian disease of regarding any hypothesis, which meets certain minimal requirements, as perfectly acceptable in science, however extravagant, or 'bold', it might be. Scientists themselves do not usually see the matter this way, however; most of them judge a hypothesis very much the worse for being based on insufficient evidence. Bacon, it seems to me, was on the side of commonsense and in tune with scientific practice in insisting that hypotheses need to be solidly based on evidence before they can be adopted, and that the more speculative they are, the more evidence they require.

Not everything that Bacon said is congenial to the present reading, however; for instance, the confident assertion in the midst of his model investigation into the nature of heat, that "after the rejection and exclusion has been duly made, there will remain at bottom, all light opinions vanishing into smoke, a form affirmative, solid, and true and well defined" (NO II, xvi). This sounds as if the exclusion process was a finite one which could exhaust all but one of the theoretical possibilities; and since the rejections of which Bacon spoke all involved observable phenomena, this remark certainly lends credence to the traditional interpretation.

But as I mentioned earlier, Bacon seems immediately to have drawn back from his confident assertion, saying that the process by which the form is achieved is more difficult than it sounds. It may be that, as is often stated, Bacon was forced into a rapid revision of his programme after realizing the difficulties involved in specifying all the simple natures. However, I think this unlikely, in the light of the rest of his philosophy; in particular, when one considers the insistence throughout his work that the real causes which constitute forms are in the configurations of minute and invisible particles. Moreover, he nowhere advocated directly that an induction should be preceded by an exhaustive analysis of compound bodies into their constituent simple natures; he merely claimed that, as compound bodies are complexes of simple natures, it would be easier to start by investigating their forms, rather than the forms of the bodies themselves, and, secondly, that when it comes to effecting significant changes in the world, like transmuting one substance into another, a knowledge of the simple natures of the substance we wish to prepare is most useful.

Another significant argument in favour of the traditional interpretation comes from those remarks of Bacon's suggesting that his method is machine-like and that it "places all wits and understandings nearly on a level". This seems to argue that hypotheses were excluded from Bacon's science, for the invention of new and interesting speculations is clearly not a skill that everybody possesses in equal measure. However, there is reason to think that too much has been read into what were merely suggestive images. This is most apparent, I believe, from the context in which Bacon presented the machine analogy. He asked us to consider the task of moving a vast obelisk. To attempt this "with naked hands", he said, would be "mad", and no less so than if the contractors increased the number of workers and engaged only the most athletic and strongest:

> A similar demented zeal [Bacon asserted] inspires our
> intellectual efforts. Men apply their naked, or unaided,
> intellect to the task. From the mere number or quality of the
> minds engaged they hope great things. By dialectics, the
> athletic part of the mind, they strengthen their mental
> sinews. But they do not bring in machines to multiply and
> combine their individual efforts. And, as due aids are not
> supplied to the mind, so nature is studied without due
> attention. (RP, 128–9)

Bacon's point I think was this: just as a machine can vastly speed up the work of many people labouring with their bare hands, so induction expedites intellectual understanding by a method which others were deceived into thinking required merely the accumulation of more and more observations or the deployment of greater dialectical skills. Bacon repeated the analogy, making the same point, in his preface to the *Novum Organum.*

Bacon's comparison of scientific method with the drawing of a circle by means of a compass was certainly an unfortunate one, whose exact significance I cannot expound with complete confidence, though I suggest it may have been an over-expansive metaphor, perhaps intended to boost enthusiasm in his readers, or to persuade them that science was not so esoteric a business as it seemed to be, especially in the hands of the alchemists, whose secretiveness was notorious.

Although some parts of Bacon's writings may perhaps lend support to the standard, infallible-mechanical interpretation, I believe that, when considered overall, those writings are in much better agreement with the hypothetico-inductive reading that I have described. That is to say, Bacon recommended that the axioms of science should be hypotheses or speculations, particularly ones concerning the latent physical causes of surface phenomena. He was not in favour, however, of unbridled speculation, in which hypotheses of the most general nature are adopted in the first instance, for he believed that the generality of one's assumptions should be increased only gradually and should be proportioned at every stage to the available evidence. The rôle of observation and experiment was both to suggest appropriate axioms and to examine those axioms, either confirming or disconfirming them. I believe that this is an essentially correct description of the method of science.

Bacon's many insights into the conduct of experimental science, and the threats which could thwart it, are extremely valuable and all the more impressive for having been discovered without the benefit of twentieth-century hindsight. Bacon's celebrity as a philosoher of science has sunk since the seventeenth and early eighteenth centuries, when he earned the title of "Father of Experimental Philosophy": it is time, I think, for his achievements once more to be acknowledged, and for the title to be restored to him.

Bibliography

Alexander, A. B. D.   1907.   *A Short History of Philosophy.*   Glasgow: James Maclehose.

Aubrey, J.   1972.   *Brief Lives,*   edited by Oliver Lawson Dick. London: Penguin Books.

Bailey, C.   1928.   *The Greek Atomists and Epicurus.*   Oxford: Clarendon Press.

Barlow, W.   1616.   *Magneticall Aduertisements: or, diuers pertinent obseruations, and approued experiments concerning the nature and properties of the Load-stone, etc.*   London.

Benjamin, P.   1895.   *The Intellectual Rise in Electricity; A History.*   New York: D. Appleton and Company.

Boas, M.   1951.   "Bacon and Gilbert",   *Journal of the History of Ideas*, vol. 12, 406–7.

Boyle, R.   1661.   *Certain Physiological Essays, written at distant times, and on several occasions.*   London.

Boyer, C. B.   1952.   "William Gilbert on the Rainbow",   *American Journal of Physics*, vol. 20, 416–21.

Brougham, H.   1856.   *The Works of Henry, Lord Brougham,*   vol. 6. London: Richard Griffin.

Cajori, F.   1929.   *A History of Physics*   (a revised and enlarged edition of a book first published in 1899). New York: The Macmillan Company.

Cassirer, E.   1953.   *The Platonic Renaissance in England*   (a translation, by J. T. Pettegrove, of *Die Platonische Renaissance in England und die Schule von Cambridge*, 1932). London: Nelson.

Church, R. W.   1909.   *Bacon.*   London: Macmillan and Company.

Cohen, L. J.   1980.   "Some Historical Remarks on the Baconian Conception of probability",   *Journal of the History of Ideas*, vol. 41, 219–31.

Cohen, M. R.   1949.   *Studies in Philosophy and Science.*   New York: Henry Holt and Company.

Dampier, W. C. D.   1929.   *A History of Science, and its Relations with Philosophy and Religion.*   Cambridge: Cambridge University Press.

Debus, A. G.   1966.   *The English Paracelsians.*   New York: Franklin Watts.

Dickie, W. M.   1922.   "A Comparison of the Scientific Method and Achievement of Aristotle and Bacon", *Philosophical Review*, vol. 31, 471–94.

Digby, Sir K.   1644.   *Two Treatises. In the one of which, the nature of bodies; in the other, the nature of man's soule; is looked into: in way of discovery, of the immortality of reasonable soules.*   Paris.

Dijksterhuis, E. J.   1969.   *The Mechanization of the World Picture.*   Oxford: Oxford University Press.

Ducasse, C. J.   1966.   "Francis Bacon's Philosophy of Science". In *Theories of Scientific Method: The Renaissance through the Nineteenth Century,*   E. H. Madden, ed. Seattle: University of Washington Press.

Duhem, P.   1908.   *To Save the Phenomena*   (translated by E. Doland and C. Maschler). Chicago: University of Chicago Press.

Ellis, R. L.   1857a.   General Preface to Spedding, Ellis, and Heath (1857–8), vol. I, 21–67.

————.   1857b.   Preface to   *Descriptio Globi Intellectualis.*   Spedding, Ellis, and Heath, 1857–8, vol. III, 715–26.

Farrington, B.   1964.   *The Philosophy of Francis Bacon.*   Liverpool: Liverpool University Press.

Frankel, H.   1979.   "The Career of Continental Drift Theory: An Application of Imre Lakatos' Analysis of Scientific Growth to the Rise of Drift Theory",   *Studies in History and Philosophy of Science*, vol. 10, 21–66.

Franklin, A. and Howson, C.   1985.   "Newton and Kepler, A Bayesian Approach",   *Studies in History and Philosophy of Science*, vol. 16, 379–85.

Fulke, W.   1560.   *Anti-prognosticon.*   London.

Gauquelin, M.   1974.   *Cosmic Influences on Human Behaviour*   (translated from the French text of 1973 by E. Clemow). London: Garnstone Press.

Gibson, R.   1950.   *Francis Bacon: A Bibliography of his Works and of Baconiana.*   Oxford: Scrivener Press.

Gilbert, W.   1600.   *De Magnete*   (translated in 1893 by P. F. Mottelay). Reprinted New York: Dover Publications, 1958.

Glanvill, J.   1676.   *Essays on Several Important Subjects in Philosophy and Religion.*   London.

Gregory, J. 1938. "Chemistry and Alchemy in the Natural Philosophy of Sir Francis Bacon, 1561-1626", *Ambix*, vol. 2, 93–111.

Grosart, A. B. 1865. *Lord Bacon not the Author of "The Christian Paradoxes"*. Edinburgh: privately printed.

Grünbaum, A. 1976. "Is Falsifiability the Touchstone of Scientific Rationality?" In *Essays in Memory of Imre Lakatos*, R. S. Cohen, P. K. Feyerabend, and M. Wartofsky, eds., 213–52. Dordrecht: D. Reidel.

Hacking, I. 1984. "Experimentation and Scientific Realism". In *Scientific Realism*. J. Leplin, ed. Berkeley: University of California Press.

Hale-White, Sir W. 1927. *Bacon, Gilbert and Harvey*. London: John Bale, Sons & Danielson.

Hall, A. R. 1983. *The Revolution in Science, 1500-1750*. London: Longman.

Harré, R. 1965. "Gilbert". In *Early Seventeenth Century Scientists*, R. Harré, ed., 1–24. Oxford: Pergamon.

Harvey, W. 1628. *De Motu Cordis et Sanguinis* (translated as *The Motion of the Heart and Blood in Animals* by R. Willis). London: J. M. Dent.

Hempel, C. G. 1965. *Aspects of Scientific Explanation*. New York: The Free Press.

_____. 1966. *Philosophy of Natural Science*. Englewood Cliffs, New Jersey: Prentice-Hall, Inc.

Hesse, M. 1964. "Francis Bacon". In *A Critical History of Western Philosophy*, J. O'Connor, ed., 142–52. New York: The Free Press of Glencoe.

Hicks, R. D., translator 1925. *Lives of Eminent Philosophers* by Diogenes Laertius. London: Heinemann.

Hochberg, H. 1953. "The Empirical Philosophy of Roger and Francis Bacon", *Philosophy of Science*, vol. 20, 313–26.

Horton, M. 1973. "In Defence of Francis Bacon", *Studies in History and Philosophy of Science*, vol. 4, 241–78.

Horwich, P. 1982. *Probability and Evidence*. Cambridge: Cambridge University Press.

Howson, C. 1973. "Must the Logical Probability of Laws be Zero?", *The British Journal for the Philosophy of Science*, vol. 24, 153–63.

——————. 1977. "Why Once May be Enough", *The Australasian Journal of Philosophy,* vol. 55, 142–6.

Howson, C., ed. 1976. *Method and Appraisal in the Physical Sciences: The Critical Background to Modern Science 1800-1905.* Cambridge: Cambridge University Press.

Jardine, L. 1974. *Francis Bacon, Discovery and the Art of Discourse.* Cambridge: Cambridge University Press.

Jevons, W. S. 1909. *Elementary Lessons in Logic: Deductive and Inductive.* London: Macmillan & Company.

Jones, R. F. 1961. *Ancients and Moderns* (second edition). Washington University Press. (Reprinted New York: Dover Publications, 1982.)

Jonson, B. 1641. *Timber: or Discoveries.* In *Ben Jonson,* C. H. Herford, P. Simpson and E. Simpson. Oxford: Clarendon Press, 1947.

Kargon, R. H. 1966. *Atomism in England from Harriot to Newton.* Oxford: Clarendon Press.

Kelley, S. 1965. *The "De Mundo" of William Gilbert.* Amsterdam: Menno Hertzberger and Company.

Kiernan, M. 1985. *Sir Francis Bacon: The Essays or Counsels, Civill and Morall.* Oxford: Clarendon Press.

Kirk, G. S., Raven, J. E. and Schofield, M. 1983. *The Presocratic Philosophers* (second edition of G. S. Kirk and J. E. Raven, 1957. Cambridge: Cambridge University Press.

Lakatos, I. 1970. "Falsificationism and the Methodology of Scientific Research Programmes". In *Criticism and the Growth of Knowledge,* I. Lakatos and A. Musgrave, eds., 91–196. Cambridge: Cambridge University Press.

Macaulay, T. B. 1837. "Lord Bacon", *Edinburgh Review,* July.

Meyerson, E. 1930. *Identity and Reality* (translated by K. Loewenberg from third edition of *Identité et Realité,* 1926). London: George Allen and Unwin.

Medawar, P. E. 1974. "More Unequal than Others", *New Statesman,* vol. 87, 50–1.

Musgrave, A. 1980. "Wittgensteinian Instrumentalism", *Theoria,* vol. 46, 63–105.

Osiander, A. 1543. Preface to *De Revolutionibus* (translated by E. R. Rosen, 1939). 24–5.

Popkin, R.   1964.   *The History of Scepticism from Erasmus to
Descartes.*   New York: Harper and Row.
Popper, K.   1959.   *The Logic of Scientific Discovery.*   London:
Hutchinson.
——————.   1962.   *The Open Society and its Enemies*   (fourth
edition). London: Routledge and Kegan Paul.
——————.   1963.   *Conjectures and Refutations.*   London: Routledge
and Kegan Paul.
——————.   1972.   *Objective Knowledge.*   Oxford: Clarendon Press.
——————.   1973.   "Evolutionary Epistemology". In *A Pocket Popper,*
D. Miller, ed. [1983] Oxford: Fontana Paperbacks.
Quinton, A.   1980.   *Francis Bacon.*   Oxford: Oxford University Press.
Rawley, W.   1657.   "The Life of the Honourable Author", in *Works* I
pp. 3–18.
Rees, G.   1975a.   "Francis Bacon's Semi-Paracelcian Cosmology",
Ambix, vol. 22, 81–101.
——————.   1975b.   "Francis Bacon's Semi-Paracelcian Cosmology
and the Great Instauration",   *Ambix,* vol. 22, 161–173.
——————.   1980.   "Atomism and 'Subtlety' in Francis Bacon's
Philosophy",   *Annals of Science,* vol. 37, 549–71.
Roller, D. H. D.   1953.   "Did Bacon Know Gilbert's *De
Magnete?*",   *Isis,* vol. 44, 10–13.
Rosen, E. R.   1959.   *Three Copernican Treatises*   (second edition).
New York: Dover Publications.
Rossi, P.   1968.   *Francis Bacon: From Magic to Science*   (translated
from the Italian text of 1957 by S. Rabinovitch). London: Routledge
and Kegan Paul.
Russell, B.   1946.   *History of Western Philosophy.*   London: George
Allen and Unwin.
——————.   1969.   'Preface' to Nicod's 'The Logical Problem of
Induction', in J. Nicod's   *Geometry and Induction.* London:
Routledge and Kegan Paul.
Singer, C.   1929.   "Bacon".   In *Encyclopaedia Brittanica* (fourteenth
edition).
Sorley, W. R.   1920.   *A History of English Philosophy.*   Cambridge:
Cambridge University Press.
Spedding, J.   1862–74.   *The Letters and the Life of Francis Bacon*
(seven volumes). London: Longman, Green, Longman, and Roberts.

——————. 1878.   *An Account of the Life and Times of Francis Bacon* (two volumes). London: Trübner and Co.

——————. 1881.   *Evenings with a Reviewer or Macaulay and Bacon* (two volumes). London: Kegan Paul, Trench & Company.

Spedding, J., Ellis R. L., and Heath, D. D., eds.   1857–8.   *The Works of Francis Bacon.*   London: Longman and Company.

Sprat, T.   1667.   *The History of the Royal Society of London for the improving of natural knowledge.*   London.

Storck, J.   1931.   "Francis Bacon and Contemporary Philosophical Difficulties",   *The Journal of Philosophy,* vol. 28, 169–86.

Taylor, F. S.   1939.   *A Short History of Science.*   London: William Heinemann.

Thorndike, L.   1958.   *A History of Magic and Experimental Science,*   vol. 7. New York: Columbia University Press.

Urbach, P.   1978.   "The Objective Promise of a Research Programme". In *Progress and Rationality in Science,* G. Radnitzky and G. Andersson, eds., 79–93. Dordrecht: D. Reidel.

——————. 1981.   "On the Utility of Repeating the 'Same' Experiment",   *The Australasian Journal of Philosophy,* vol. 59, 151–62.

——————. 1982.   "Francis Bacon as a Precursor to Popper",   *The British Journal for the Philosophy of Science,* vol. 33, 113–32.

Voltaire, F. M. A. de   1734.   *Lettres philosophiques.*   Amsterdam.

Ward, S.   1654.   *Vindicae Academiarum. Containing some briefe animadversions upon Mr Webster's book, stiled, The Examination of Academies etc.*   [Signed, H.D.]. Oxford.

Whewell, W.   1857.   *History of the Inductive Sciences.*   Reprinted, 1967. Frank Cass & Co. Ltd., London.

Index

ad hoc adjustments to theories
    anticipation of nature, 27, 31-32,
      51, 125, 128-129
    interpretation of nature, 53-54
    Popper, Karl, 32-33, 51, 53
Advancement of Learning, The
    (1605; abbreviated herein as
    AL), 7, 12
    alchemy, 32, 107, 125
    causation, 101
    definition of words, 93
    Gilbert, William, 111, 115
    mathematics, 136-137
alchemy, 51, 71, 97, 109, 125
Alexander, A. B. D., 84
alphabet of nature, 70-72, 190-191
analogy: SEE prerogative instances
    of
ancient (Greek) science: SEE
    astronomy; atomism; poverty
    of science
anticipation, Epicurus on, 37-38
anticipation of evidence by theory,
    53-54
anticipation of nature (method
    criticized by Bacon), 25-30
    (SEE ALSO alchemy;
      astrology; astronomy;
      Gilbert; interpretation of
      nature)
    ad hoc adjustments to theories,
      27, 31-32, 51, 125, 128-129
    breadth of theories, 27-29
    confirmation and prediction,
      27-28, 30, 50-52, 96, 122-123
    dogmatism, 27-28, 36
    enumeration, 29-30
    logic, 142

order (chronological) of
    discovery, 53-54
poverty of contemporary science,
    27-28, 31-32, 145
speculation and generalization,
    34-36, 55, 97
under the standard
    interpretation, 20, 25-26, 33,
    38
Apophthegms, 11
arithmetic, 136
Aristotle, 2, 80, 130, 135, 140
    method, of, 96, 101-102, 142
Arundel, Earl of, 6
astrology, 87, 121-125, 158
astronomy
    conventionalism, 30-32
    diurnal motion, 113, 115-119,
      130-134
    hypotheses, 126-130, 141, 153
    and physics, 126-128
atheism, 99-100
atomism, 68, 72-78
    spirits, 75-76
    the vacuum, 73-74, 77-81
Aubrey, John, 5-6, 143
Augustus Caesar, 11
axioms, 27-28, 33-35, 155-156 (SEE
    ALSO generalization;
    hypotheses)
    in the hierarchy of knowledge,
    67

Bacon, Francis: SEE life of Bacon;
    writings by Bacon summarized
Bacon, Sir Nicolas (father of
    Francis), 1-2

Bailey, C., 75
Barlow, William, 120
Bayes's theorem, 56
Benjamin, P., 109
Berkeley, George, 37
Bertholet, Pierre, 155
Bible: SEE religion
biography of Bacon (1561-1626), 1-7
biology, 143-147
Boas, M., 109
Boyer, C., 110
Boyle, Robert, 150
breadth of theories, 27-29, 50-51
Brougham, Lord Henry, 100-101

Cajori, F., 26, 39
Carnap, R., 58
Cassirer, E., 26
causal explanation, 60, 62 (SEE
    ALSO final causes)
Cecil, Sir William (Lord Burleigh),
    1-2
celestial bodies: SEE astrology;
    astronomy
certainty, 49, 188 (SEE ALSO
    infallibility)
  in astronomy, 125-128, 132
  as extreme degree of confidence,
    43, 189
  generalization, 55, 67
  histories, natural and
    experimental, 157-160
  plausibility, 55-56
  probable conjectures, 30, 46-48
  under the standard
    interpretation, 17-18, 39
  use of term in Bacon's time,
    44-46, 126-127
*Cogitata et Visa de Interpretatione
  Naturae:* SEE *Thoughts and
  Conclusions*

Cogitationes de Natura Rerum:
    SEE *Thoughts on the Nature
    of Things*
Cohen, L. J., 41, 44, 68-69, 162
Cohen, M. R., 23, 26, 84, 108
cold: SEE heat
Collection of Collections: SEE
    Sylva Sylvarum
colour, 63-64, 67, 139, 168-169
compound (concrete) bodies: SEE
    forms
conditions, necessary and
    sufficient, 60, 62, 64-66, 177
  Bacon's investigation of heat,
    174-175
confirmation and disconfirmation of
    theories (SEE ALSO
    prediction)
  anticipation of nature, 30, 32,
    96-97, 122-123
  dogmatism, 86-88
  interpretation of nature, 28, 33,
    91, 155-156
  prerogative instances of Alliance
    and Divorce, 166-167
  sense-perception, 91-92
conjecture, 30, 46-48 (SEE ALSO
    hypotheses)
conventionalism (instrumentalism),
    30-33
Copernicus, 115, 125-134 *passim*
cosmology: SEE astronomy
crucial experiment, 19, 169-171
  of Gilbert's theories, 115, 133
Cupid (and atomism), 10, 68, 74

Dampier, W. C. D., 152
Darwin, Charles, 101
De Augmentis Scientiarum (1623
    revision of *The Advancement
    of Learning;* abbreviated
    herein as DA), 7, 12

astrology, 121-124
astronomy, 128-132
causation, 101-102
conjecture, 30
doubts, 160-161
forms, 70
instances, natural histories, 154
knowledge and understanding,
    66-67, 104-105
mathematics, 136, 138, 140
medicine, 144-146
religion, 98, 102-105
De Sapientia Veterum (On the
    Wisdom of the Ancients, 1609),
    10, 68, 74
Debus, A. G., 103
definitions: SEE idols of the
    Market-place
Democritus, 72-75, 77-78, 102, 183
density and rarity, 79-81, 139, 174
Decartes, René, 137, 177
Descriptio Globi Intellectualis:
    SEE NEXT ENTRY
*Description of the Intellectual
    Globe, A* (Descriptio Globi
    Intellectualis, 1612;
    abbreviated herein as DIG),
    10, 12
    astronomy, 128-131, 134, 157-158
    conventionalism, 32
    monsters, 161-162
    observation and theory, 157-158
developmental process in physical
    bodies, 60-61
Dickie, W. M., 154-156
Digby, Sir Kenelm, 44
Dijksterhuis, E. J., 135
Diogenes Laertius, 37-38, 115
diurnal motion, 113, 115-121, 130,
    134
dogmatism, 27-28, 31-32, 35-36
    idols of the mind, 86-88, 98-99

Ducasse, C. J., 15
Duhem, P., 32

editions of Bacon's works used,
    11-12
efficient causes, 60
Elizabeth I, 1-4, 11
elementary and compound: SEE
    forms
Ellis, Robert, 11, 14, 17-18, 23, 39,
    93-94, 126, 155
empirical idols of the mind, 96-98,
    153, 155
enumeration of instances: SEE
    instances
Epicurus's anticipations, 37-38
Essays, 7, 11
essence, 135, 140 (SEE ALSO
    forms)
Essex, Earl of, 3
euthanasia, 146
evidence, 33, 53-54, 151-152,
    154-156 (SEE ALSO instances)
experiment: SEE histories, natural
    and experimental

facts (SEE ALSO instances)
    collection
        number, 151-155
        variety, 89, 154, 161-164, 172,
            174
    incorrigibility, 156-160
    relation of theory to, 150-151,
        154-156, 158
fallibility: SEE infallibility
falsification of theories: SEE
    confirmation
falsificationism, 49-51, 56 (SEE
    ALSO Popper)
Farrington, B., 12
final causes, 60, 68, 100-102 (SEE
    ALSO metaphysics)

finiteness of nature (under the
    standard interpretation), 18-19
First Vintage, 179-183
formal causes, 60-62
forms, 62-63
  atomism, 72
  colour and heat, 63-66, 139
  compound or concrete, 19-20,
    69-70, 153-154
  elementary or simple: SEE
    forms: compound
  exhibited in degrees, 176-177
  in hierarchy of knowledge,
    66-69, 71
  and natures, 19-20, 62-63,
    153-154, 176-178
  prerogative instances, 164-171
  Quantity as a form, 140
  under the standard
    interpretation, 19-22, 70-71,
    153-154
Frankel, H., 53
Franklin A., 54
frivolous distinction: SEE *ad hoc*
Fulke, William, 44-45

Galileo, 26, 132, 170
Gauquelin, M., 124
generalization, 34-36 (SEE ALSO
    speculation)
  and certainty, 54-57, 67
  hierarchy of knowledge, 66-69
geometry, 136
Gilbert, William (1544-1603), 45,
    96, 126
  in Bacon's writings, 109-113, 120,
    170
  diurnal motion, 113, 115-119
  magnetism, terrestrial, 113-115,
    117-119
  publication of theories, 109-110
  teleological argument, 118, 120

Glanvill, Joseph, 45
gradualism: SEE generalization
gravity, 170-171
Great Instauration, The: SEE *Plan*
Greek (ancient) science: SEE
    astronomy; atomism; poverty
    of science
Gregory, J., 75
Grosart, A. B., 103
Grünbaum, A., 15

Hacking, I., 171
Hale-White, Sir W., 143
Hall, A. R., 112
Hanson, N. R., 31
Harré, R., 112
Harvey, William (1578-1657), 44,
    48, 143-144
heat, 154, 156, 166-167
  interpretation of nature, 179-183
  as motion, 63-66, 68-69, 180,
    182-183
  sensations, 54
  tables
    of degrees, 176-178
    of instances (presence or
      absence), 172-176
Heath, Douglas D., 11
heliocentricity: SEE astronomy
Hempel, C. G., 53, 101
heresy and heterodoxy, 98-100, 102,
    104-105
Hero (of Alexandria), 73
Hesse, M., 14-15, 19, 39, 76, 80,
    84, 142
heterogeneous instances: SEE
    instances
Hicks, R. D., 37, 115-116
hierarchy of knowledge, 66-69
Hippocrates, 145
histories, natural and experimental
    (SEE ALSO instances)

collection of facts, 151-154,
161-164
contents, 157
crucial experiments, 19, 169-171
of Gilbert's theories, 115, 133
incorrigibility, 156-160
under the standard
interpretation, 150-160 *passim*
History of Dense and Rare, The
(1658) 8, 139
History of Life and Death, The
(1623), 8, 145, 147
Hochberg, H., 137
Hooke, Robert, 150
Horton, M., 15, 62, 134, 190
Howson, C., 46, 52, 54
Hume, David, 131
hypotheses, hypothetical reasoning
(SEE ALSO infallibility;
observation)
astronomical, 125-130, 141
'hypothetico-inductive' method,
15, 108, 192
speculation and generalization,
34-36, 54-55, 112, 126
under the standard
interpretation, 20, 22-23, 26,
33-34, 150-151
working, 155-156

idols (of the mind), 20
of the Cave (individual human
nature), 87-90
of the Market-place (linguistic),
92-95
tabula rasa, 84-85, 157
of the Theatre (philosophical),
95-96
empiricism and rationalism,
96-98
final causes, 100-102
superstition, 98-100

theology, 102-105
of the Tribe (general human
nature), 86-87, 100
induction: SEE anticipation of
nature; instances;
interpretation of nature;
supports of induction
infallibility (SEE ALSO certainty)
under the standard
interpretation, 38-39, 188-192
astronomy, 125-126
histories, natural and
experimental, 150-151,
156-160
'infallible-mechanical' thesis,
14, 17-23, 42, 191-192
sense-perception, 90
use of concept in Bacon's time,
126-127
inspiration, intuition, 17, 23, 26
(SEE ALSO speculation)
instances
enumeration
Bacon's investigation of heat,
172-178
simple, 29-30, 153-154
heterogeneous, 89, 154, 172, 174
prerogative, 154, 164, 171-172,
180
configuration of world
(Analogy), 167
establishing hypotheses
(Fingerpost), 169-171
exhibiting natures (Striking or
Shining; Solitary), 168-169,
180
indirect observation, 165
initial observations, 164-166
of the Lamp, 165-166, 181
mathematical, 138-139, 165
refuting hypotheses (Alliance
and Divorce), 166-167

tables (for investigation of heat),
172-176
'instauration' defined, 7
instrumentalism (conventionalism),
30-33
interpretation of nature (method
advocated by Bacon), 25 (SEE
ALSO anticipation of nature)
breadth of theories, 28-29
confirmation and prediction, 28,
41, 50, 91, 156
exclusion of putative causes,
178-179, 182-183
and falsificationism, 49-51, 56
First Vintage; Bacon's
investigation of heat, 179-183
hypotheses, hypothetical
reasoning, 34-36, 155-156
plausibility, 54-56
sense-perception 91-92
speculation and generalization,
34-36, 55-56, 91
under the standard
interpretation, 20, 25-26, 179

James I, 4
Jardine, L., 29, 125, 135
Jeffreys, Sir H., 58
Jevons, W. S., 26
Jones, R. F., 111, 126
Jonson, Ben, 3

Kargon, R. H., 76
Kelley, S., 109
Kepler, Johannes, 26, 129
Keynes, J. M., 58
Kiernan, M., 7
Kirk, G. S., 116
knowledge: goals of science, 66-69,
71
knowledge and power, 60

Lakatos, I., 52-54
latent configurations and processes,
60-61
laws: SEE forms
Leucippus, 183
life of Bacon (1561-1626), 1-7
light, 142
limited variety, principle of, 19
Lives of Eminent Philosophers
(Diogenes Laertius), 38
loadstone: SEE magnetism
Locke, John, 84
logic, 140-143
Lucretius, 38

Macaulay, Lord, 7
Mach, Ernst, 31
magic, 140-141
magnetism, 112-115, 116-119
Masculine Birth of Time (Temporis
Partus Masculus, 1603;
abbreviated herein as MBT), 9,
12, 125
idols of the mind, 85
induction by anticipation of
nature, 30
material causes, 60
mathematics
applied (mixed), 136-139
handmaid of physics, 140-143
in metaphysics, 140-141
pure, 136-137, 143
value for natural science, 134-143
'mechanical' interpretation: SEE
infallibility
mechanics, 140-141
Medawar, P. E., 52
medicine, 144-147
Harvey, William, 143-144
metaphysics (SEE ALSO forms)
applied: magic, 140-141

in the hierarchy of knowledge,
66-69
and mathematics, 140-141
scope of, 60-62
method, scientific: Bacon's
summarized, 13-15 (SEE
ALSO anticipation of nature;
interpretation of nature)
Meyerson, E., 155
Mill, John Stuart, 23, 57
motion, diurnal, 113, 115-121,
130-134
motion the form of heat, 63-65,
68-69, 180, 182-183
Münchhausen, Baron, 40
Musgrave, A., 31

natural history: SEE histories,
natural and experimental
natural kinds, 94-95, 161-162
natures of bodies: SEE forms
necessary conditions: SEE
conditions
New Atlantis, The, 10
New Organon: SEE *Novum
Organum*
Newton, 130, 169-170
Nicodemus, 104
Novum Organum (New Organon,
1620; abbreviated herein as
NO), 8, 12
anticipation of nature, 48
Aristotle, 96, 102
astrology, 122
astronomy, 132-133, 162
atomism and the vacuum, 77-79
breadth of theories, 28-29
causation, 100
certainty, 18-19, 55
confirmation and prediction, 28,
50, 89-90

conjectures, 47-48
definition of words, 92-93
dogmatism, 36, 86-88
forms, 62-63, 68-69, 71, 164-165,
176-177, 179
Gilbert, William, 111-112, 114-115
gravity, 75, 171
heat, 172-178, 180
idols (of the mind), 85
of the Cave, 87-89
of the Market-place, 92-95
of the Theatre, 96, 98-100,
102-103
of the Tribe, 85-87, 90
induction, 25, 28, 33, 42,
178-179, 183
instances, natural histories, 154,
159, 162-163, 172, 181
prerogative, 164-171, 180
tables of, 172-174
interpretation of nature, 48,
179-183
mathematics, 138-139
observation and theory, 155-156
poverty of science, 25-29
proof methods, 40-41
province of physics, 60-61
rationalism and empiricism,
96-98
reasonableness of engaging in
research (SEE ALSO *De
Augmentis:* religion), 42-43
religion, theology, 99, 102-103
speculation and generalization,
34-36, 89, 91
superstition, 99, 122
theory and application, 77
words, 92-95

observation and theory, 155-156
(SEE ALSO hypotheses;
instances)

conventionalism
　(instrumentalism), 30-32
indirect, 165
and poverty of science, 27-28
under the standard
　interpretation, 20, 150-151,
　154-155
operative (applied) science, 59, 71
Osiander, 127

Paracelsus, 103
*Parasceve ad Historiam et
　Naturalem* (Preparative
　Towards a Natural and
　Experimental History, 1620),
　8, 151-152, 157
Pascal's wager, 42-43
Paulet, Sir Amias, 2
pet theories, 86-88
Phenomena of the Universe, The
　(five works, 1620-1658), 8
Philolaus, 115-116
philosophia prima, 67
philosophical systems: SEE idols of
　the Theatre
philosophy, natural, 97-98
　versus astronomy, 126-128
　in the hierarchy of knowledge,
　　67-68
physics
　applied: mechanics, 140-141
　versus astronomy, 126-128
　in the hierarchy of knowledge,
　　66-69
　and logic, 140-143
　and mathematics, 134-140
　　mathematics the handmaid of
　　　physics, 140-143
　scope of, 60-61
Plan of the Great Instauration
　(abbreviated herein as *Plan*),
　7-9, 12

experiments, 158-159
history of science, 107-108
idols of the mind, 84-85
induction by simple
　enumeration, 29
logic, 142
mechanical nature of method, 18
sense-data, 158-159
tabula rasa, 84-85
Plato, 100, 126
plausibility, 51-58
Plinius, Caius, 6
pneumatic theory of matter, 75-76
Popkin, R., 90
Popper, Karl
　"adhocness", 32-33, 51, 53, 86-87
　falsificationism, 49-52, 56-58, 122
　hypothesis and certainty, 23, 26,
　　34, 46, 126, 141
　tabula rasa; idols of the mind,
　　84-88, 90
　ultimate explanations, 152-153
poverty of science (natural
　philosophy) (SEE ALSO
　alchemy; astrology; astronomy;
　medicine)
　ancient Greek, 2, 13, 35-36, 96,
　　100
　contemporary science, 13, 27-30
　conventionalism
　　(instrumentalism), 30-33
　under the standard
　　interpretation, 107-108
prediction (SEE ALSO
　confirmation)
　anticipation of nature, 27, 32,
　　50-52
　interpretation of nature, 28, 41,
　　50-51, 53-54, 155-156
prerogative instances: SEE
　instances
presuppositions: SEE idols of the
　Market-place

probable conjecture, probable
reasoning, 30, 46-48
progress in the sciences: natural
history, 151-152
proof
of induction method, 39-42
use of term in Bacon's time,
44-46
properties of natural objects: SEE
forms
Ptolemy, 126, 128, 130, 134
Pythagoras, 74

quantity: SEE mathematics
Quinton, A., 131, 134-135, 138

rarity and density, 79-81, 139, 174
rational idols of the mind, 96-98
Rawley, William, 2, 6
Redargutio Philosophiarum: SEE
Refutation of Philosophies
Rees, G., 10, 74-76, 79
Refutation of Philosophies, The
(Redargutio Philosophiarum,
1608; abbreviated herein as
RP), 9, 12
Aristotle, 96
empiricism, 96-97
experience and theory, 14
speculation and dogmatism, 35
Reichenbach, H., 58
religion
Bacon's faith, 10-11, 98-99,
103-105
heresy, 98-100, 102, 104
prohibition of research, 99-100,
103-105
superstition, 98-100
theology, 102-104
Roller, D. H. D., 110
Rosen, E., 127
Rossi, P., 15

Russell, Bertrand, 108, 148
Ryle, Gilbert, 31

science
deficiencies in: SEE poverty of
science
in the hierarchy of knowledge,
66-69, 71
operative and speculative, 59-60,
71
scientific method: Bacon's
summarized, 13-15 (SEE
ALSO anticipation of nature;
interpretation of nature)
sensations of heat and cold, 64
sense-impressions, sense-
perceptions
histories, natural and
experimental, 158-159
and speculation, 90-91
Shakespeare *(Othello),* 44
simple enumeration of instances:
SEE instances
simple natures (properties) SEE
forms
Simplicius, 127
Singer, C., 153
Sorley, W. R., 153
speculation, 47 (SEE ALSO
generalization)
astronomical, 125-130
dangers in, 34-36, 89-91
and poverty of science, 27, 31
and sense-perception, 90-91
under the standard
interpretation, 20, 23, 26,
90-91, 112-113
speculative science, 59-60
Spedding, James, 6, 11-12, 93-94,
132
spirit(s), 75-76, 147
Sprat, Thomas, 150

'standard interpretation' of Bacon,
    14-15, 17-23 (SEE ALSO
    anticipation of nature;
    certainty; forms; histories,
    natural and experimental;
    hypotheses; infallibility;
    interpretation of nature;
    observation and theory;
    poverty of science;
    speculation)
Storck, J., 34
structure of physical bodies, 60-61
substances: SEE forms
sufficient conditions: SEE
    conditions
superstition, 98-100 (SEE ALSO
    religion)
summary law of nature, summary
    philosophy, 67-68
supports of induction, 180-181
Sylva Sylvarum (Collection of
    Collections, 1627; abbreviated
    herein as Sylva), 8, 12, 149-150
    atomism, 78
    gravity, 170-171
    light and sound, 76
    superstition, 98

tables of instances and degrees,
    172-178
tabula rasa, 84-85, 157
Taylor, F. S., 110
Temporis Partus Masculus: SEE
    Masculine Birth of Time
terminology of Bacon's time, 44-48,
    126-127
testability (SEE ALSO
    confirmation; prediction), 50,
    52, 155-156
Thema Coeli: SEE *Theory of the
    Heaven*
theology (SEE ALSO religion)

danger of confounding with
    science, 102-105
theoretical entities, 31-32, 49,
    90-92, 165
theories: SEE hypotheses;
    observation
Theory of the Heaven (Thema
    Coeli, 1612; abbreviated herein
    as TH), 10, 12
    astronomy, 128-133
Thorndike, L., 101, 135, 137
*Thoughts and Conclusions on the
    Interpretation of Nature*
    (Cogitata et Visa de
    Interpretatione Naturae, 1607;
    abbreviated herein as TC), 9,
    12
    breadth of theories, 29
    generalization, 55
    Gilbert, William, 111, 115
    poverty of science, 27
    theology and religion, 102-103
Thoughts on the Nature of Things
    (Cogitationes de Natura
    Rerum, 1604), 73, 76, 80
Tycho Brahe, 128, 134

uncertainty: SEE certainty
universality: SEE generalization

vacuum, existence of, 73-74, 77-82
*Valerius Terminus of the
    Interpretation of Nature*
    (1603); abbreviated herein as
    VT), 9, 12
    astronomy, 131-132
    causation, 60
    forms, 63-64, 67
variety of instances: SEE instances,
    heterogenous
vivisection, 146
Voltaire, 170

Ward, Seth, 134-135
weight: atoms and spirits, 75
Whewell, William, 57, 131
Whitgift, John (Archbishop of
    Canterbury), 2
Wittgenstein, Ludwig, 31
words: SEE idols of the Market-
    place
Works (edition in seven volumes),
    11-12
working hypotheses, 155-156
Wright, Edward, 120-121
writings by Bacon summarized,
    7-12

Xenophanes, 115-116